RUSSIAN PICTURE DICTIONARY COLORING BOOK

Over 1500 Russian Words and Phrases for Creative & Visual Learners of All Ages

Color and Learn

Lingo Mastery

Free Book Reveals the 6-Step Blueprint That Took Students **from Language Learners to Fluent in 3 Months**

- **6 Unbelievable Hacks** that will accelerate your learning curve

- **Mind Training:** why memorizing vocabulary is easy

- **One Hack to Rule Them All:** This <u>secret nugget</u> will blow you away...

Head over to **LingoMastery.com/hacks** and claim your free book now!

CONTENTS

INTRODUCTION

This **Russian Picture Dictionary Coloring Book** is a fun vocabulary building tool with illustrations that you can color while studying. It covers an immense range of topics that will help you learn everything related to the Russian language in daily subjects, from members of the family and animals to parts of the body and describing jobs.

This introduction is a guide to help you get started in Russian and polish your basic grammar, spelling, punctuation, and vocabulary skills. Good luck – and **most importantly, enjoy yourself!**

BASICS OF THE RUSSIAN LANGUAGE

I. Reading and pronunciation rules

a. Vowels

There are ten letters in the Russian language that are used to indicate vowels: А, О, У, И, Э, Ы, Е, Ё, Ю, Я.

Let's see how they are pronounced, and in what way they will be indicated in transcription in this book. The first six are quite simple:

Letter/pronunciation	Example
Аа – [a] - like 'a' in 'car'.	ананас – [ana-NAS] – *pineapple*
Оо – [o], [ə] - like 'o' in 'more'. - in unstressed syllables it can be pronounced either as the previous [a] sound or as a neutral vowel – [ə] (like the second 'e' in 'letter').	море – [MO-r'eh] – *sea* гора – [ga-RA] – *mountain* розовый – [RO-zə-vyj] – *pink*

Уу – [u] - like 'oo' in 'moon', but not as prolonged.	мука – [mu-KA] – *flour*
Ии – [i] - like 'ea' in 'leaf', but not as prolonged. - makes the preceding consonant sound soft.	лист – [l'ist] – *leaf*
Ээ – [eh] - like the first 'e' in 'elephant', but a bit more closed.	эхо – [EH-hə] – *echo*
ы – [y] – there is no capital letter - there is no similar sound in the English language. - to pronounce letter 'ы', put your lips in the position for pronouncing the English 'ee' sound, but start pronouncing 'oo'.	ты – [ty] – *you*

The last four letters (Е, Ё, Ю, Я) can be pronounced in different ways depending on their position in the word. There are several pronunciations depending on two kinds of positions:

Position one includes three options:

- at the beginning of a word
- after a vowel
- after the soft and the hard signs – 'ь' and 'ъ'

Position two includes the rest of the cases, while the vowels in this position make the preceding consonant sound soft.

Position one	Position two
Ее – [j+eh] **like 'ye' in 'yes'** ель – [jehl'] – *fir tree*	**Ее – [eh]** **like 'e' in 'end'** лето – [L'EH-tə] – *summer*
Ёё – [j+o] **like 'yo' in 'yogurt'** ёж – [josh] – *hedgehog*	**Ёё – [o]** **like 'o' in 'orange'** лёд – [l'ot] – *ice*
Юю – [j+u] **like 'you'** юг – [jug] – *South*	**Юю – [u]** **like 'oo' in 'moon'** люди – [L'U-d'i] – *people*
Яя – [j+a] **like 'yu' in 'yummy'** яхта – [JAH-tə] – *yacht*	**Яя – [a]** **like 'a' in car** рядом – [R'A-dəm] – *next to*

b. Consonants

Familiarize yourself with these phonetic phenomena before going over to studying consonants.

1) Voicing and devoicing

There are voiced and voiceless consonants in Russian. Such sounds exist in English as well. For example, 'D' is voiced and 'T' is voiceless.

Voiced consonants are more intense and need the work of the vocal cords to be produced.

Voiceless sounds are the ones that don't require the work of the vocal cords to be produced. They are more relaxed and the air flows freely from the lungs to the mouth.

Depending on their position in the word, voiced consonants can become voiceless and vice versa, which is called devoicing and voicing accordingly.

Voicing: when a voiceless consonant occurs before a voiced consonant, it undergoes voicing.

Экзамен – [eh**g**-**Z**A-m'ehn] – *exam*

Devoicing: when a voiced consonant occurs at the end of a word or before a voiceless consonant, it undergoes devoicing.

Кра**б** – [кra**p**] - *crab*

Most consonants form the so called voiced-voiceless pairs. Here they are:

Voiced	Voiceless
Бб	Пп
Вв	Фф
Гг	Кк
Дд	Тт
Жж	Шш
Зз	Сс

If you fail to observe voicing or devoicing, it will not influence the sense of the word. However, it's worth paying attention to these phenomena to sound more natural.

2) Soft and hard consonants

Depending on their 'neighbors', Russian consonants can sound either hard or soft. Most consonants can be both hard and soft, while some of them are always hard or always soft.

Consonants that can be both hard and soft

Б	В	Г	Д	З	К	Л	М	Н	П	Р	С	Т	Ф	Х
Б'	В'	Г'	Д'	З'	К'	Л'	М'	Н'	П'	Р'	С'	Т'	Ф'	Х'

The following vowels can make these consonants sound soft:

Ее, Ёё, Юю, Яя, and Ии

And of course, letter 'ь' or soft sign has the same effect on preceding consonants. In the rest of the cases these consonants sound hard.

Лилия – [L'I-l'i-ja] – *lily*

Мяч – [m'ach] – *ball*

The following consonants are always hard regardless of the following vowel:

Жж, Шш, Цц

Even when they are followed by Ее, Ёё, Юю, Яя, Ии or the soft sign (ь) they are still hard.

Шея – [SHEH-ja] – *neck*

The following consonants are always soft regardless of the following vowel:

Чч, Щщ, Йй

So we won't be using the softness indicator ['] with them.

Человек – [cheh-la-V'EHK] – human being

Note that while we use the softness marker – ['] to indicate soft vowels, we won't be doing this for these consonants because they are always soft.

There is one more point to pay attention to before you go over to the consonants. Compare these words in order to avoid the possible confusion with reading the [eh] transcription sign:

Тело – [T'EH-lə] – *body*

[eh] is read like 'e' in 'end' and makes 't' soft.

Уважение – [u-va-ZHEH-n'i-jeh] – *respect*

The first [eh] is read like the first 'e' in 'elephant', since 'ж' is always hard.

The second 'eh' is read like 'ye' in 'yes'.

Экономика – [eh-ka-NO-m'i-ka] – *economy*

[eh] is read like the first 'e' in 'elephant', since it phonetically depicts the sound of the letter 'э'.

We suggest you go back to these examples whenever you may feel confused with reading and pronouncing this sound.

Russian consonants

Letter/pronunciation	Example
Бб – [b], like 'b' in 'bear'.	банк – [bank] – *bank*
Вв – [v], like 'v' in 'video', but not so intense.	ветер – [V'EH-t'ehr] – *wind*
Гг – [g], like 'g' in 'get'.	год – [got] - *year*
Дд – [d], like 'd' in 'dear', but with your tongue on the teeth and not on the palate like in English.	дом – [dom] – *house*
Жж – [zh], this sound is a bit special. To understand how to pronounce it, say 'jam'. And now try to exclude the 'd' sound from it. The consonant you get is [zh].	жена – [zheh-NA] – *wife*
Зз – [z], like 'z' in 'zoo'.	зонт – [zont] – *umbrella*
Йй – [j], like 'y' in 'yoga'.	йод – [jot] – *iodine*
Кк – [k], like 'c' in 'cat', but unlike in English, the sound is never aspirated.	кот – [kot] – *cat*
Лл – [l], like 'l' in 'lemon', but with your tongue on the teeth and not on the palate like in English.	лиса – [l'i-SA] – *fox*
Мм – [m], like 'm' in 'milk'.	молоко – [ma-la-KO] – *milk*
Нн – [n], like 'n' in 'nose', but with your tongue on the teeth and not on the palate like in English.	нос – [nos] – *nose*
Пп – [p], like 'p' in 'pipe', unlike in English, the sound is never aspirated.	папка – [PA-pka] – *folder*

Рр – [r], like 'r' in 'river', but the tip of your tongue should be on the front part of your palate, and not on the back one like in English.	рука – [ru-KA] – *hand*
Сс – [s], like 's' in snow, but with your tongue on the palate, and not on your teeth like in English.	сок – [sok] – *juice*
Тт – [t], like 't' in 'tiger', but with your tongue on the teeth, and not on the palate like in English.	тигр – [t'igr] – *tiger*
Фф – [f], like [f] in 'film', just a bit more relaxed.	фото – [FO-tə] – *photo*
Хх – [h], like 'h' in 'home'.	хлеб – [hl'ehp] – *bread*
Цц – [ts], like the combination of [t] and [s] sounds.	цунами – [tsu-NA-m'ï] – *tsunami*
Чч – [ch], like 'ch' in 'chicken'.	час – [chas] – *hour*
Шш – [sh], like 'sh' in 'shy'.	шорты – [SHOR-ty] – *shorts*
Щщ – [sch], like the combination of [s] and [ch] sounds.	щит – [schit] – *shield*
ь – gives no sound, just makes the preceding consonant soft. Is never capitalized.	семь – [s'ehm'] – *seven*
ъ – gives no sound, just makes the preceding consonant hard. Is never capitalized.	объём – [ab-JOM] – *volume*

Special cases that contradict reading rules

You see	You read	Example
-его and -ого	-ево and -ово [jeh-VO] and [ə-və]	его – *him, his* [jeh-VO]
-ться and -тся	-цца [tsa]	смеяться – *laugh* [sm'eh'-JA'tsa]
letter 'чт' (rarely)	letter 'ш' [sh]	что – *what* [shto]
letter 'й' (only in the word you see in the example)	not read	сейчас – *now* [s'e-CHAS]

Mute Consonants

There are some words in the Russian language that feature consonants clusters in which one of the consonants is not pronounced. During your exciting journey of learning Russian, you will come across these words and remember how to pronounce them. For now, you can familiarize yourself with some of the most widespread words containing mute consonants.

The underlined letters are mute. Read and remember these words.

здрав-ствуй-те – [ZDRA-stvuj-t'eh] – *hello*

сер-дце – [S'EHR-tseh] – *heart*

сол-нце – [SON-tseh] – *sun*

грус-тный – [GRU-snyj] – sad

II.   Grammar

Russian grammar is rather intense, since the relationship between words is expressed through endings. Pronouns, nouns, adjectives, and verbs change their endings depending on the grammatical category and the patterns for these changes require lots of knowledge and practice.

Since grammar is not the major goal of this book, this section includes only basic things, such as what grammatical categories mean and what forms different parts of speech can take, while learning how exactly to build these forms will be the aim of other books.

a. Pronouns

Categories of pronouns:

- Person (1st, 2nd, 3rd)
- Number (singular and plural)
- Case (see the table below)
- Gender (only for 3rd person singular)

Cases of personal pronouns

Nominative	Genitive Posselion	Dative InDirect object	Accusative Direct object	Instrumental	Prepositional
Я – I 1st person singular	Меня	Мне	Меня	Мной	Мне
Ты – You 2nd person singular	Тебя	Тебе	Тебя	Тобой	Тебе
Мы – We 1st person plural	Нас	Нам	Нас	Нами	Нас
Вы – You 2nd person plural	Вас	Вам	Вас	Вами	Вас
Он – He 3rd person singular masculine	Его	Ему	Его	Им	Нём
Она – She 3rd person singular feminine	Её	Ей	Её	Ею	Неё
Оно – It 3rd person singular neutral	Его	Ему	Его	Им	Нём
Они – They 3rd person plural	Их	Им	Их	Ими	Них

11

Possessive pronouns

Personal pronoun	Possessive pronoun
я – I	мой – my/mine
ты – you	твой – your/yours
мы – we	наш – our/ours
вы – you	ваш – your/yours
он – he	его – his
она – she	её – her/hers
оно – it	его – its
они – they	их – their

Possessive pronouns and their gender, number, and cases

Gender / Number	Nominative	Genitive	Dative	Accusative Animate	Accusative Inanimate	Instrumental	Prepositional
Masculine Singular	Мой	Моего	Моему	Моего	Мой	Моим	Моём
	Твой	Твоего	Твоему	Твоего	Твой	Твоим	Твоём
	Наш	Нашего	Нашему	Нашего	Наш	Нашим	Нашем
	Ваш	Вашего	Вашему	Вашего	Ваш	Вашим	Вашем
Feminine Singular	Моя	Моей	Моей	Моей		Моей	Моей
	Твоя	Твоей	Твоей	Твоей		Твоей	Твоей
	Наша	Нашей	Нашей	Нашей		Нашей	Нашей
	Ваша	Вашей	Вашей	Вашей		Вашей	Вашей
Neutral Singular	Моё	Моего	Моему	Моё		Моим	Моём
	Твоё	Твоего	Твоему	Твоё		Твоим	Твоём
	Наше	Нашего	Нашему	Наше		Нашим	Нашем
	Ваше	Вашего	Вашему	Ваше		Вашим	Вашем
Plural	Мои	Моих	Моим	Моих	Мои	Моими	Моих
	Твои	Твоих	Твоим	Твоих	Твои	Твоими	Твоих
	Наши	Наших	Нашим	Наших	Наши	Нашими	Наших
	Ваши	Ваших	Вашим	Ваших	Ваши	Вашими	Ваших

Note that possessive pronouns 'его' (masculine), 'её' (feminine), and 'их' (all genders) are the same for all numbers, and cases, so they are not included into the table.

13

b. Nouns

Categories of nouns:

- Gender
- Number
- Case

Gender of nouns

There are three genders in Russian: **masculine, feminine, and neuter (neutral)**. Very often grammatical gender is attributed to the noun according to physical gender, like in 'мать' – 'mother', which is feminine.

With other nouns, especially inanimate ones, it's different and the gender should be defined by an ending of the noun in its initial form, apart from a few exceptions.

Masculine	Feminine	Neutral
The last letter of the word is **consonant** or '**й**'. For example: Певец – *Singer* Нищий – *Beggar*	The last letter is '**а**' or '**я**'. For example: Профессия – *Profession* Книга – *Book*	The last letter is '**о**' or '**е**'. For example: Окно – *Window* Море – *Sea*

Exceptions to the rule that occur due to physical gender:

папа – *dad* (masculine)

дядя – *uncle* (masculine)

дедушка – *grandfather* (masculine)

мужчина – *man* (masculine)

Number of nouns

Noun type	Ending in plural form	Example
- masculine noun that ends in **a hard consonant** - feminine nouns ending in **-а**	**-ы** **- ы, - и**	**стол – столы** table – tables **мама – мамы** mother – mothers **чашка – чашки** cup – cups
- all nouns ending in **-ь, -й, -я**	**-и**	**зверь – звери** beast – beasts **дядя – дяди** uncle – uncles
- masculine and feminine nouns with the stem ending in **-к, -г, -х, -ч, -щ, -ж, -ш**	**-и**	**нога – ноги** leg – legs **муха – мухи** fly – flies
- neutral nouns ending in **-о**	**-а**	**окно – окна** window – windows
- neutral nouns ending in **-е**	**-я**	**море – моря** sea – seas

Exceptions:

ребёнок – дети

child – children

человек – люди

person – people

брат – братья

brother – brothers

Cases of nouns – singular

Case	Endings		
	Masculine	**Feminine**	**Neutral**
Nominative	Consonant, -й, -ь	-а, -я, -ь,	-о, -е, -мя
Genitive	-а, -я	-ы, -и	-а, -я, -мени
Dative	-у, -ю	-е, -ии, -и	-у, -ю, -мени
Accusative Animate	-а, -я		
Accusative Inanimate	Accusative = Nominative	-а, -я, -ь	Accusative = Nominative
Instrumental	-ом, -ем	-ой, -ей, ь+ю	о+м, е+м, -менем
Prepositional	Consonant + e, -е	-е, -ии, -и	-е, -и, -мени

Cases of nouns – plural

Case	Endings		
	Masculine	**Feminine**	**Neutral**
Nominative	-ы, -и	-ы, -и, -ии	-а, -я, -ия
Genitive	Consonant + ов, -ей, -ев	-a removed, -ь, -ий, -ей	-о removed, -ий, -ей
Dative	-ам, -ям		
Accusative Animate	Consonant + ов, -ев, -ей	-a removed, -ь, -ий, -ей	Accusative = Nominative
Accusative Inanimate	Accusative = Nominative	Accusative = Nominative	
Instrumental	-ами, -ями		
Prepositional	-ах, -ях		

c. Adjectives

Adjectives coincide with the nouns they define in gender, number, and case.

Masculine – Singular		
	hard ending (-ой, ый)	soft ending (-ий)
Nominative	молодой – *young*	синий – *blue*
Genitive	молодого	синего
Dative	молодому	синему
Accusative	молодой/ого	синий/его
Instrumental	молодым	синим
Prepositional	молодом	синем

Feminine – Singular		
	hard ending (-ая)	soft ending (-яя)
Nominative	молодая	синяя
Genitive	молодой	синей
Dative	молодой	синей
Accusative	молодую	синюю
Instrumental	молодой	синей
Prepositional	молодой	синей

Neutral – Singular		
	hard ending (-ое)	soft ending (-ее)
Nominative	молодое	синее
Genitive	молодого	синего
Dative	молодому	синему
Accusative	молодое	синее
Instrumental	молодым	синим
Prepositional	молодом	синем

Plural – All genders		
	hard ending (-ые)	soft ending (-ие)
Nominative	молодые	синие
Genitive	молодых	синих
Dative	молодым	синим
Accusative	молодые/ых	синие/их
Instrumental	молодыми	синим/ими
Prepositional	молодых	синих

d. Verbs

Categories of verbs (included minimum)

- Person (1st, 2nd, 3rd)
- Tense

Present Tense

Russian present tense corresponds to the English present simple, present continuous, and present perfect continuous.

Pronoun/Person	Ending	Example
я (1st person singular)	-ю	Я игра**ю**. – *I play.*
ты (2nd person singular)	-ешь, -ишь	Ты игра**ешь**. – *You play.* Ты говор**ишь**. – *You say.*
он, она (3rd person singular)	-ет, - ит	Она игра**ет**. – *She plays.* Он говор**ит**. – *He says.*
мы (1st person plural)	-ем, -им	Мы игра**ем**. – *We play.* Мы говор**им**. – *We say.*
вы (2nd person plural)	-ете, -ите	Вы игра**ете**. – *You play.* Вы говор**ите**. – *You say.*
они (3rd person plural)	-ют, -ят	Они игра**ют**. – *They play.* Они говор**ят**. – *They say.*

Past Tense

Russian past tense corresponds to the English past simple, past continuous, present perfect, past perfect, and past perfect continuous.

The ending depends on the gender of subject, i.e. the doer of the action.

Masculine	**-л**
Купить – *buy*	
Папа (он) купил продукты на рынке. – Dad (he) bought foodstuffs at the market.	
Feminine	**-ла**
Приехать – *come by vehicle*	
Моя сестра (она) приехала сюда на поезде. – My sister (she) came here by train.	
Neutral	**-ло**
Прийти – *arrive*	
Письмо (оно) пришло утром. – The letter (it) arrived in the morning.	
Plural	**-ли**
Фотографировать – *take photos*	
Туристы фотографировали собор. – The tourists were taking photos of the cathedral.	

Future Tense

Russian future tense corresponds to the English future simple, future simple continuous, future perfect, and future perfect continuous.

Person	Compound form *быть + infinitive*	Simple form *infinitive conjugated according to the rules of the present tense*
я – I	буд**у** играть – *will play*	поигра**ю** – *will have played*
ты – you	буд**ешь** играть	поигра**ешь**
мы – we	буд**ем** играть	поигра**ем**
вы – you	буд**ете** играть	поигра**ете**
он/она/оно – he/she/it	буд**ет** играть	поигра**ет**
они – they	буд**ут** играть	поигра**ют**

III. A few peculiarities that are essential for better understanding

The verb 'быть – to be'

Compare these sentences in Russian and English:

Я пилот – I am a pilot

These sentences mean the same but have a different number of words. The thing is that the Russian verb 'to be – быть' is omitted in the present tense. **Compare more examples:**

Она из Америки. – She is from America.

Они шумные. – They are noisy.

Они мои родители. – They are my parents.

Я врач. – I am a doctor.

Types of sentences and their word order

Affirmative sentences

In the English language, affirmative sentences always follow the Subject (S) + Verb (V) + Object (O) pattern, while in Russian this structure can be rather flexible. The S+V+O pattern is the most widespread one, but you can also come across O+V+S or V+S+O options.

The difference between them is in the shades of meaning.

Example:

Мы играли в футбол. – We were playing football. – Neutral meaning.

В футбол играли мы. – The same translation with the emphasis on the kind of sport we were playing. That was football and not volleyball or hockey.

Играли мы в футбол. – The emphasis is on the action.

Conclusion: You can play with word order in affirmative sentences, but whenever you feel not confident enough, go for the conventional S+V+O structure and you'll make no mistake.

Negative sentences

There are three particles in Russian that help express negation. They are **'нет', 'не', and 'ни'**.

Take a look at these examples to get a general idea without going into much detail.

Ты рано встаёшь по выходным? – *Нет, по выходным я встаю поздно.*

Do you wake up early on weekends? – *No, I don't*. *I wake up late at weekends*.*

В комнате **нет** врача. – *There is no doctor in the room.*

У меня **нет собаки**. – *I don't have a dog.*

Я **не** люблю танцевать. – *I don't like dancing.*

Эта машина **не** моя. – *This car is not mine.*

У неё нет **ни** детей, **ни** мужа. – *She's got neither kids nor husband.*

*In Russian, there is negation and affirmation in one sentence and this is absolutely normal. First you negate the question about waking up early and then say that you wake up late in the same sentence.

Interrogative sentences

Finally, unlike in English, interrogative sentences in Russian don't require any grammatical change of the sentence. If it's **a question with the question word**, we just add it to the initial affirmative sentence, make the corresponding changes in pronouns, and change the intonation.

For example:

Меня зовут Аня. – The question to the sentence is: **Как тебя зовут**?

Мне семь лет. – The question to the sentence is: **Сколько тебе лет**?

If it's **a yes/no question**, we simply change the pronoun and the intonation.

For example:

У меня есть семья. – The question to the sentence is: **У тебя есть семья**?

Я говорю по-немецки. – The question to the sentence is: **Ты говоришь по-немецки**?

Now, let's get started with the content!

ЭМОЦИИ (EMOTIONS)

1) **счастливый** (happy)
schas-L'I-vyj

2) **грустный** (sad)
GRUS-nyj

3) **рад** (excited)
rat

4) **злой** (angry)
zloj

5) **удивлённый** (surprised)
u-d'iv-L'ON-nyj

6) **озабоченный** (concerned)
a-za-BO-chehn-nyj

7) **напуганный** (scared)
na-PU-gan-nyj

8) **любопытный** (curious)
l'u-ba-PYT-nyj

9) **изумлённый** (amused)
i-zum-L'ON-nyj

10) **сбитый с толку** (confused)
ZB'I-tyj s TOL-ku

11) **больной** (sick)
bal'-NOJ

12) **капризный** (naughty)
kap-R'IZ-nyj

13) **серьёзный** (serious)
s'eh-R'OZ-nyj

14) **сосредоточенный** (focused)
sas-r'eh-da-TO-chehn-nyj

15) **незаинтересованный** (bored)
n'eh-za-in-t'eh-r'eh-SO-van-nyj

16) **потрясённый** (overwhelmed)
pa-tr'a-S'ON-nyj

17) **влюблённый** (in love)
vl'ub-L'ON-nyj

18) **пристыженный** (ashamed)
pr'is-TY-zhehn-nyj

19) **взволнованный** (anxious)
vzval-NO-van-nyj

20) **чувствующий отвращение**
(disgusted)
CHUS-tvu-ju-schij   at-vra-SCHEH-n'i-jeh

21) **обиженный** (offended)
a-B'I-zhehn-nyj

22) **опечаленный** (sore)
a-p'eh-CHA-l'ehn-nyj

Почему ты такой злой сегодня?
Why are you so angry today?

На работе он всегда сосредоточенный.
He is always focused at work.

Мои коллеги сбиты с толку этим проектом.
My colleagues are confused with this project.

СЕМЬЯ (THE FAMILY)

1) **дедушка и бабушка** (grandparents)
   D'EH-dush-ka i BA-bush-ka

2) **бабушка** (grandmother)
   BA-bush-ka

3) **дедушка** (grandfather)
   D'EH-dush-ka

4) **дядя** (uncle)
   D'A-d'a

5) **мама** (mother)
   MA-ma

6) **папа** (father)
   PA-pa

7) **тётя** (aunt)
   T'O-t'a

8) **двоюродный брат** (cousin, m.)
   dva-J'U-rad-nyj brat

9) **брат** (brother)
   brat

10) **я** (me)
    j'a

11) **муж/жена** (husband/wife)
    myzh/zheh-NA

12) **сестра** (sister)
    s'ehs-TRA

13) **двоюродная сестра** (cousin, f.)
    dva-J'U-rad-na-ja s'ehs-TRA

14) **племянник** (nephew)
    pl'eh-M'AN-n'ik

15) **сын** (son)
    syn

16) **дочь** (daughter)
    doch

17) **племянница** (niece)
    pl'eh-M'AN-n'i-tsa

18) **внук** (grandson)
    vnuk

19) **внучка** (granddaughter)
    VNU-chka

20) **троюродный брат/сестра** (second cousin)
    tra-J'U-rad-nyj brat/s'ehs-TRA

• **Семья мужа/жены (In-laws) – Родственники (Relatives)**

   S'ehm'-J'A MU-zha/zheh-NY
   – ROT-stv'ehn-n'i-k'i

21) **свёкор/тесть** (father-in-law)
    sv'okr/t'ehst'

22) **свекровь/тёща** (mother-in-law)
    sv'ehk-ROF'/T'O-scha

23) **деверь/шурин** (brother-in-law)
    D'EH-v'ehr'/SHU-r'in

24) **золовка/свояченица** (sister-in-law)
    za-LOF-ka/sva-J'A-cheh-n'i-tsa

25) **невестка** (daughter-in-law)
    n'eh-V'EHS-tka

26) **зять** (son-in-law)
    z'at'

27) **дядя мужа/жены** (uncle-in-law)
    D'A-d'a MU-zha/zheh-NY

28) **тётя мужа/жены** (aunt-in-law)
    T'O-t'a MU-zha/zheh-NY

Мой племянник уже ходит в школу.
My nephew already goes to school.

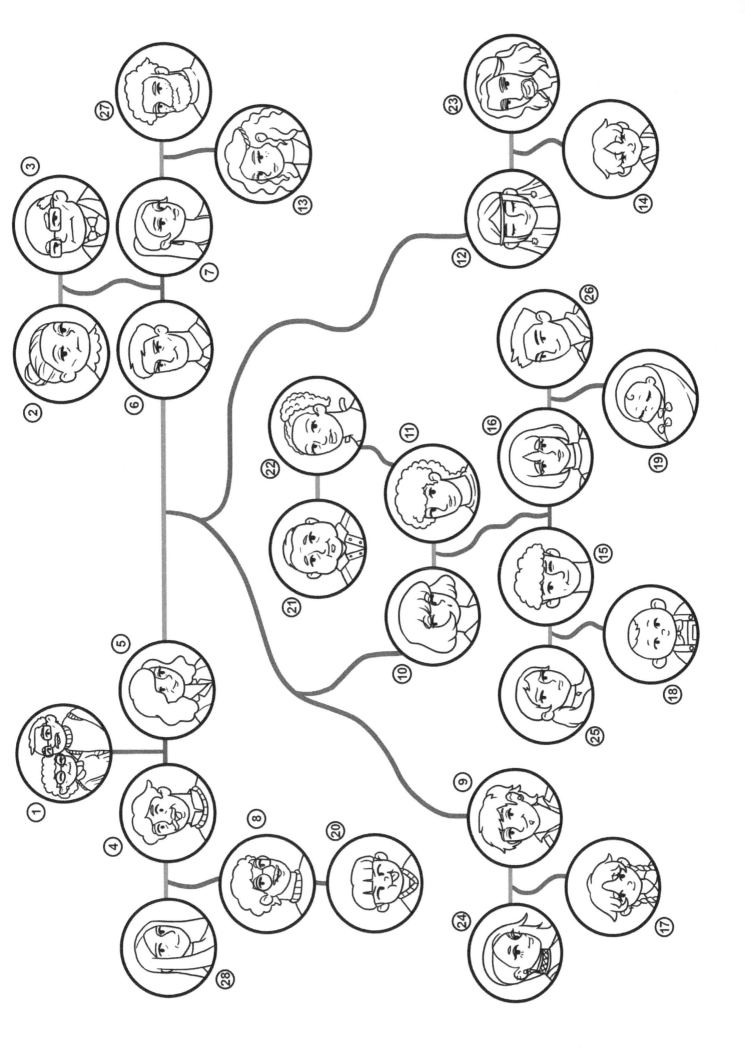

ВЗАИМООТНОШЕНИЯ (RELATIONSHIPS)

1) **женатая пара** (married couple)
zheh-NA-ta-ja PA-ra

2) **женатый мужчина** (married man)
zheh-NA-tyj muzh-CHI-na

3) **замужняя женщина** (married woman)
za-MUZH-n'a-ja ZHEHN-schi-na

4) **разведённая пара** (divorced couple)
raz-v'eh-D'ON-na-ja

5) **бывшая жена** (ex-wife)
BYF-sha-ja zheh-NA

6) **бывший муж** (ex-husband)
BYF-shyj muzh

7) **друг** (friend)
druk

8) **девушка** (girlfriend)
D'EH-vush-ka

9) **парень** (boyfriend)
PA-r'ehn'

10) **сосед** (neighbor)
sa-S'EHT

11) **неженатый/незамужняя** (single)
n'eh-zheh-NA-tyj/n'eh-za-MUZH-n'a-ja

12) **разведённый, разведённая/развод** (divorced m., f./divorce)
raz-v'eh-D'ON-nyj, raz-v'eh-D'ON-na-j'a/raz-VOT

13) **вдовец** (widower)
vda-V'EHTS

14) **вдова** (widow)
vda-VA

Паша мой лучший друг.
Pasha is my best friend.

Моя бывшая жена живёт в другом городе.
My ex-wife lives in another town.

Эта женатая пара – наши соседи.
This married couple are our neighbors.

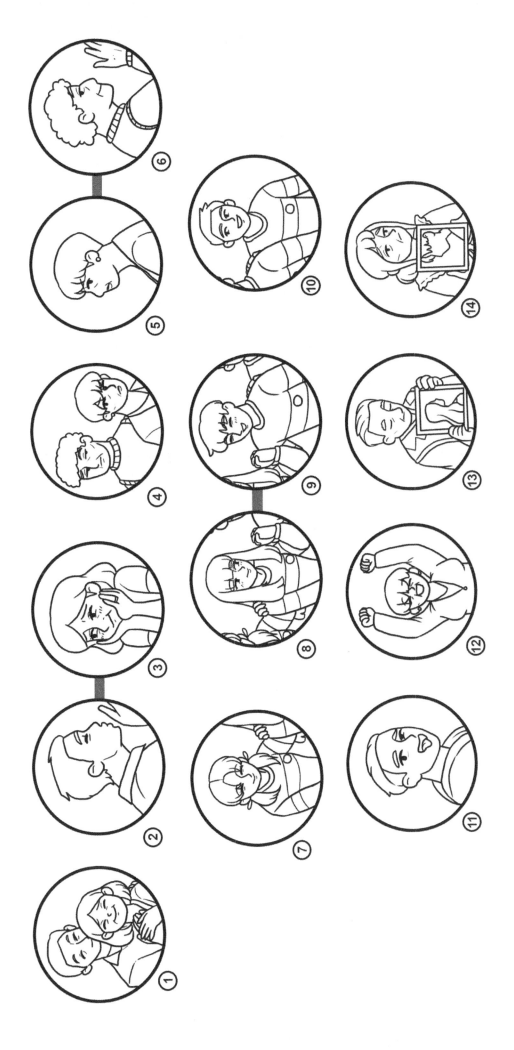

ЦЕННОСТИ (VALUES)

1) **уважение** (respect)
   u-va-ZHEH-n'i-j'eh

2) **благодарность** (gratitude)
   bla-ga-DAR-nəst'

3) **толерантность** (tolerance)
   ta-l'eh-RAN-tnəst'

4) **взаимовыручка** (mutual aid)
   vza-i-ma-VY-ruch-ka

5) **честность** (honesty)
   CHEHS-nəst'

6) **трезвость, сдержанность**
   (temperance)
   TR'EHZ-vəst', ZDEHR-zhə-nəst'

7) **ответственность** (responsibility)
   at-V'EHT-stv'ehn-nəst'

8) **вера** (faith)
   V'EH-ra

9) **мужество** (courage)
   MU-zheh-stvə

10) **доброта** (kindness)
    da-bra-TA

11) **серьёзность намерений**
    (commitment)
    s'eh-R'J'OZ-nəst' na-M'EH-r'eh-n'ij

12) **энтузиазм** (enthusiasm)
    ehn-tu-z'i-AZM

13) **доверие** (trust)
    da-V'EH-r'i-jeh

14) **пунктуальность** (punctuality)
    pun-ktu-AL'-nəst'

Я очень ценю твою честность.
I appreciate your honesty a lot.

Её доброта не знает границ.
Her kindness knows no boundaries.

Он потерял моё доверие навсегда.
He's lost my trust forever.

ТЕЛО ЧЕЛОВЕКА (THE HUMAN BODY)

1) **голова** (head)
ga-la-VA

2) **волосы** (hair)
VO-lə-sy

3) **лицо** (face)
l'i-TSO

4) **лоб** (forehead)
lop

5) **ухо** (ear)
U-hə

6) **глаза** (eyes)
gla-ZA

7) **нос** (nose)
nos

8) **щека** (cheek)
scheh-KA

9) **рот** (mouth)
rot

10) **подбородок** (chin)
pad-ba-RO-dək

11) **шея** (neck)
SHEH-ja

12) **спина** (back)
sp'i-NA

13) **грудь** (chest)
grud'

14) **плечо** (shoulder)
pl'eh-CHO

15) **рука** (arm)
ru-KA

16) **предплечье** (forearm)
pr'ehd-PL'EH-chjeh

17) **кисть** (hand)
k'ist'

18) **живот** (abdomen)
zhy-VOT

19) **талия** (waist)
TA-l'i-ja

20) **ягодица** (hip)
ja-ga-D'I-tsa

21) **нога** (leg)
na-GA

22) **бедро** (thigh)
b'eh-DRO

23) **колено** (knee)
ka-L'EH-nə

24) **икра** (calf)
ik-RA

25) **голень** (shin)
GO-l'ehn'

26) **ступня** (foot)
stup-N'A

У неё красивые голубые глаза.
She's got beautiful blue eyes.

Она упала и сломала руку.
She fell down and broke her arm.

Я делаю упражнения, чтобы спина не болела.
I do exercises so that my back doesn't hurt.

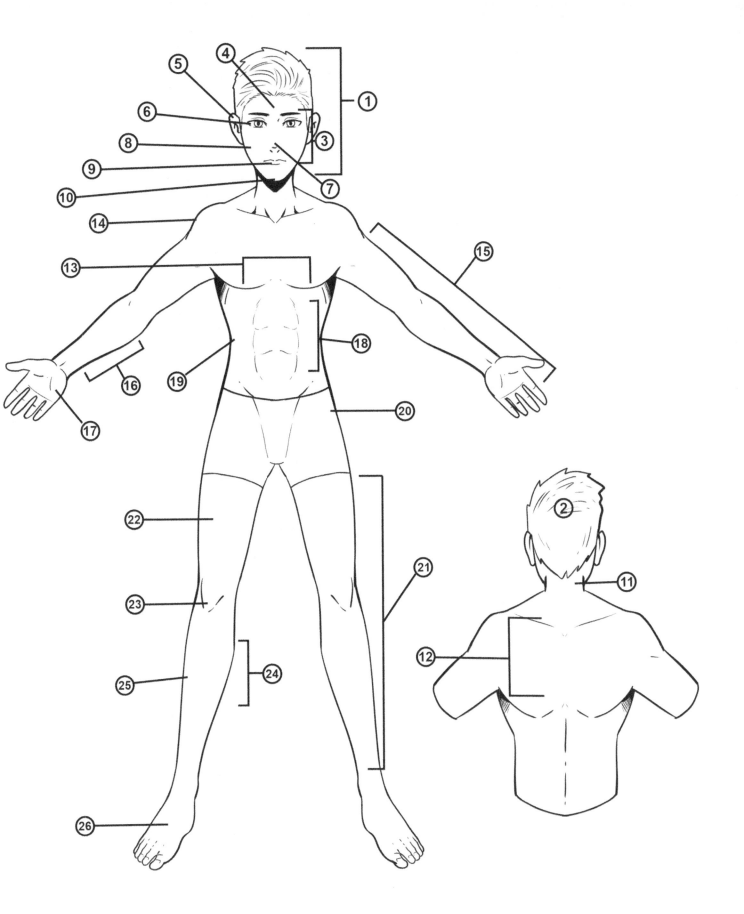

ВНУТРЕННИЕ ОРГАНЫ ЧЕЛОВЕКА (INSIDE THE HUMAN BODY)

1) **кожа** (skin)
KO-zha

2) **мышцы** (muscles)
MYSH-tsy

3) **кости** (bones)
KOS-t'i

4) **мозг** (brain)
mozg

5) **щитовидная железа** (thyroid)
schi-ta-V'ID-na-ja zheh-l'eh-ZA

6) **вены** (veins)
V'EH-ny

7) **артерии** (arteries)
ar-TE-r'i-i

8) **сердце** (heart)
S'EHR-tseh

9) **лёгкие** (lungs)
L'OH-k'i-jeh

10) **желудок** (stomach)
zheh-LU-dək

11) **пищевод** (esophagus)
p'i-scheh-VOD

12) **поджелудочная железа** (pancreas)
pad-zheh-LU-dəch-na-ja zheh-l'eh-ZA

13) **печень** (liver)
P'EH-chehn'

14) **тонкий кишечник** (small intestine)
TON-k'ij k'i-SHEH-chn'ik

15) **толстый кишечник** (large intestine)
TOLS-tyj k'i-SHEH-chn'ik

16) **жёлчный пузырь** (gallbladder)
ZHEHL-chnyj pu-ZYR'

17) **почки** (kidneys)
POCH-k'i

18) **мочевой пузырь** (urinary bladder)
ma-cheh-VOJ pu-ZYR'

У моего дедушки проблемы с сердцем.
My grandfather has issues with his heart.

Жареная еда — это плохо для желудка.
Fried food is bad for the stomach.

Ей удалили жёлчный пузырь.
She had her gallbladder removed.

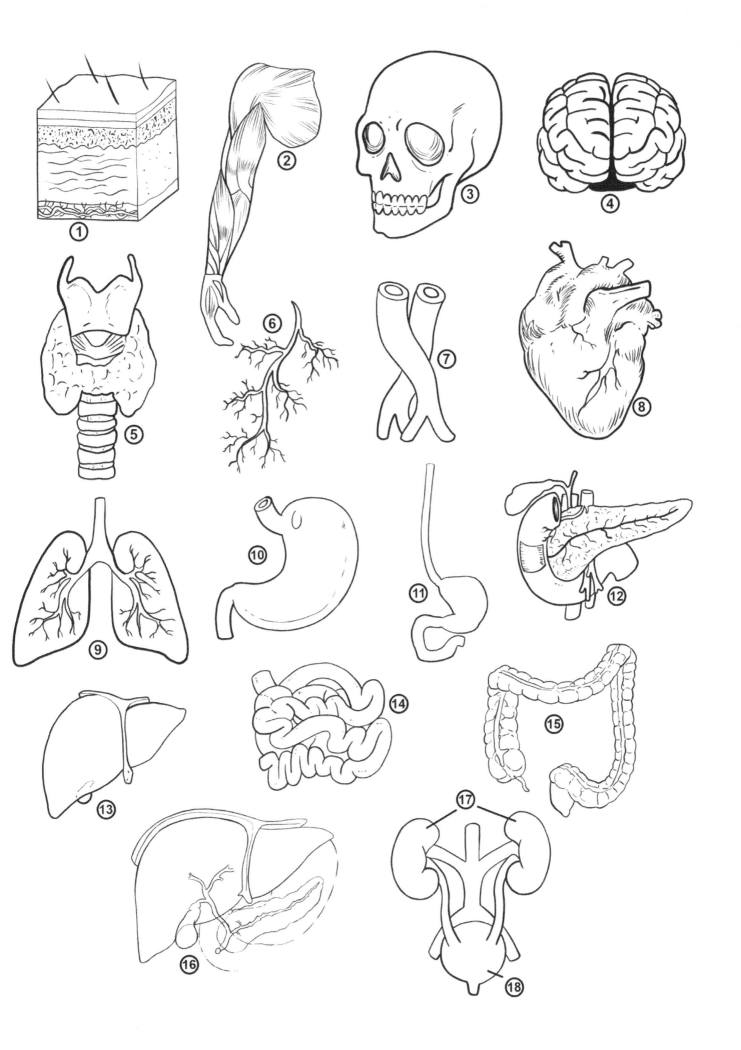

ДОМАШНИЕ ЖИВОТНЫЕ (PETS)

1) **собака** (dog)
   sa-BA-ka

2) **кот/кошка** (cat m./f.)
   kot/KOSH-ka

3) **хорёк** (ferret)
   ha-R'OK

4) **мини-пиг** (mini pig/teacup pig)
   M'I-n'i-PIG

5) **лошадь** (horse)
   LO-shad'

6) **скалярия** (angelfish)
   ska-L'A-r'i-ja

7) **рыба-клоун** (clown fish)
   RY-ba-KLO-un

8) **золотая рыбка** (goldfish)
   za-la-TA-ja RYP-ka

9) **хомяк** (hamster)
   ha-M'AK

10) **морская свинка** (guinea pig)
    mar-SKA-ja SV'IN-ka

11) **мышь** (mouse)
    mysh

12) **кролик** (rabbit)
    KRO-l'ik

13) **ёж** (hedgehog)
    josh

14) **тарантул** (tarantula)
    ta-RAN-tul

15) **колония муравьёв** (ant colony)
    ka-LO-n'i-ja mu-ra-v'jof

16) **черепаха** (tortoise)
    cheh-r'eh-PA-ha

17) **змея** (snake)
    zm'eh-JA

18) **хамелеон** (chameleon)
    ha-m'eh-l'eh-ON

19) **игуана** (iguana)
    i-gu-A-na

20) **канарейка** (canary)
    ka-na-R'EHJ-ka

21) **попугай** (parrot)
    pa-pu-GAJ

22) **попугайчик** (parakeet)
    pa-pu-GAJ-chik

У меня две собаки и одна кошка.
I've got two dogs and one cat.

Моя мама боится моего тарантула.
My mom is afraid of my tarantula.

Дядя купил моей сестре золотую рыбку.
My uncle has bought my sister a goldfish.

ЗООПАРК (THE ZOO)

1) **слон** (elephant)
slon

2) **носорог** (rhino)
na-sa-ROH

3) **жираф** (giraffe)
zhy-RAF

4) **зебра** (zebra)
Z'EH-bra

5) **бегемот** (hippopotamus)
b'eh-g'eh-MOT

6) **гепард** (cheetah)
g'eh-PART

7) **тигр** (tiger)
t'igr

8) **лев** (lion)
l'ehf

9) **шимпанзе** (chimpanzee)
shim-pan-ZEH

10) **орангутан** (orangutan)
a-ran-gu-TAN

11) **бабуин** (baboon)
ba-bu-IN

12) **кенгуру** (kangaroo)
k'ehn-gu-RU

13) **коала** (koala)
ka-A-la

14) **лемур** (lemur)
l'eh-MUR

Жираф – самое высокое животное на Земле.
The giraffe is the tallest animal on Earth.

Тигр сильнее льва.
The tiger is stronger than the lion.

Зебры похожи на лошадей.
Zebras resemble horses.

ПТИЦЫ (BIRDS)

1) **страус** (ostrich)
STRA-us

2) **павлин** (peacock)
pav-L'IN

3) **индюк** (turkey)
in-D'UK

4) **петух** (rooster)
p'eh-TUH

5) **утка** (duck)
U-tka

6) **лебедь** (swan)
L'EH-b'eht'

7) **пеликан** (pelican)
p'eh-l'i-KAN

8) **фламинго** (flamingo)
fla-M'IN-gə

9) **голубь** (pigeon)
GO-lup'

10) **сова** (owl)
sa-VA

11) **стервятник** (vulture)
st'ehr-V'AT-n'ik

12) **орёл** (eagle)
a-R'OL

13) **чайка** (seagull)
CHAJ-ka

14) **ворон** (crow)
VO-rən

15) **тукан** (toucan)
tu-KAN

16) **пингвин** (penguin)
p'ihn-GV'IN

17) **дятел** (woodpecker)
D'A-t'ehl

18) **ара** (macaw)
A-ra

19) **колибри** (hummingbird)
ka-L'IB-r'i

20) **киви** (kiwi)
K'I-v'i

Орёл – это сильная, хищная птица.
The eagle is a strong carnivorous bird.

Мне не нужен будильник, потому что у меня есть петух.
I don't need an alarm clock because I've got a rooster.

Утки обожают плавать и нырять.
Ducks love swimming and diving.

QUIZ #1

Use arrows to match the corresponding translations:

a. husband   1. собака

b. eagle   2. слон

c. naughty   3. мозг

d. dog   4. кожа

e. hair   5. вера

f. elephant   6. уважение

g. aunt   7. тигр

h. brain   8. муж

i. tiger   9. любопытный

j. daughter   10. орёл

k. faith   11. тётя

l. girlfriend   12. лебедь

m. skin   13. дочь

n. curious   14. волосы

o. respect   15. девушка

p. swan   16. капризный

Fill in the blank spaces with the options below (use each word only once):

Сегодня маленький Матвей _____. Он плачет, его лицо и _____ красные от слёз. _____ обещала отвести его в зоопарк. Матвей обожает животных. У него есть кролик, игуана и _____. Но они не могут поехать в зоопарк, потому что машина сломалась. «Матвей, не плачь, – просит бабушка. – Ты разбиваешь мне _____. Ты мой любимый _____, но я не могу починить машину сама!» Матвей понимает, но не может успокоиться. Виктор Иванович – _____ бабушки. Он предлагает отвезти их в зоопарк на своей машине. Теперь Матвей _____! Он увидел бегемота, жирафа, гепарда и даже _____! Из птиц ему очень понравились ара и _____.

«Спасибо, – говорит бабушка. – Ваша _____ спасла моего внука!»

«Не за что, – говорит Виктор Иванович. – Счастливый ребёнок – это лучшая _____».

сосед	глаза
грустный	льва
хомяк	внук
благодарность	счастливый
сердце	доброта
бабушка	киви

РЕПТИЛИИ И АМФИБИИ (REPTILES AND AMPHIBIANS)

- **Рептилии (Reptiles)**
  r'ehp-T'I-l'i-i

1) **анаконда** (anaconda)
   a-na-KON-da

2) **королевская кобра** (king cobra)
   ka-ra-L'EHF-ska-ja KOB-ra

3) **гремучая змея** (rattlesnake)
   gr'eh-MU-cha-ja zm'eh-JA

4) **коралловая змея** (coral snake)
   ka-RA-la-va-ja zm'eh-JA

5) **рогатая ящерица** (horned lizard)
   ra-GA-ta-ja JA-scheh-r'i-tsa

6) **плащеносная ящерица** (frill-necked lizard)
   pla-sche-NOS-na-ja JA-scheh-r'i-tsa

7) **обыкновенный василиск** (common basilisk/Jesus Christ lizard)
   a-byk-na-V'EN-nyj va-s'i-L'ISK

8) **комодский варан** (Komodo dragon)
   ka-MOT-sk'i-j va-RAN

9) **крокодил** (crocodile)
   kra-ka-D'IL

10) **гавиал** (gharial/gavial)
    ga-v'i-AL

11) **морская черепаха** (sea turtle)
    mar-SKA-ja che-r'eh-PA-ha

- **Амфибии (Amphibians)**
  am-F'I-b'i-i

12) **саламандра** (salamander)
    sa-la-MAN-dra

13) **лягушка-голиаф** (Goliath frog)
    l'a-GUSH-ka-ga-l'i-AF

Крокодилы жили в одно время с динозаврами.
Crocodiles lived at the same time as dinosaurs.

Королевская кобра выглядит красиво, но она очень опасна.
The royal cobra looks beautiful, but it's very dangerous.

Анаконда не ядовитая, но очень сильная змея.
The anaconda is not poisonous, but is a very strong snake.

НАСЕКОМЫЕ И ПАУКООБРАЗНЫЕ (INSECTS AND ARACHNIDS)

- **Насекомые (Insects)**
  na-s'eh-KO-my-jeh

1) **пчела** (bee)
   pcheh-LA

2) **шмель** (bumblebee)
   shm'ehl'

3) **оса** (wasp)
   a-SA

4) **жук** (beetle)
   zhuk

5) **бабочка** (butterfly)
   BA-ba-chka

6) **мотылёк** (moth)
   ma-ty-L'OK

7) **стрекоза** (dragonfly)
   str'eh-ka-ZA

8) **божья коровка** (ladybug)
   BO-zhja ka-ROF-ka

9) **светлячок** (firefly)
   sv'eh-tl'a-CHOK

10) **таракан** (cockroach)
    ta-ra-KAN

11) **слепень** (horsefly)
    SL'EH-p'ehn'

12) **муха** (fly)
    MU-ha

13) **комар** (mosquito)
    ka-MAR

14) **кузнечик** (grasshopper)
    kuz-n'EH-chik

15) **сверчок** (cricket)
    sv'ehr-CHOK

- **Паукообразные (Arachnids)**
  pa-u-ka-ab-RAZ-ny-jeh

16) **скорпион** (scorpion)
    skar-p'i-ON

17) **паук** (spider)
    pa-UK

18) **чёрная вдова** (Southern black widow)
    CH'OR-na-ja vda-VA

Многие люди боятся пауков.
Many people are afraid of spiders.

Стрекозы похожи на маленькие вертолёты.
Dragonflies resemble little helicopters.

Мою сестру ужалила оса.
My sister was stung by a wasp.

МЛЕКОПИТАЮЩИЕ I (MAMMALS I)

1) **летучая мышь** (bat)
l'eh-TU-cha-ja mysh

2) **утконос** (platypus)
ut-kə-NOS

3) **касатка** (killer whale/orca)
ka-SAT-ka

4) **дельфин** (dolphin)
d'ehl'-F'IN

5) **бобр** (beaver)
bobr

6) **сурок** (groundhog)
su-ROK

7) **крот** (mole)
krot

8) **белка** (squirrel)
B'EHL-ka

9) **ласка** (weasel)
LAS-ka

10) **опоссум** (possum/opossum)
a-PO-sum

11) **крыса** (rat)
KRY-sa

12) **заяц** (hare)
ZA-jats

13) **барсук** (badger)
bar-SUK

14) **скунс** (skunk)
skuns

15) **леопард** (leopard)
l'eh-a-PART

Опоссумы носят своих детёнышей на спине.
Possums carry their babies on their backs.

Это правда, что скунсы ужасно пахнут?
Is it true that skunks smell awful?

Говорят, что дельфины очень умные.
They say that dolphins are very intelligent.

МЛЕКОПИТАЮЩИЕ II (MAMMALS II)

1) **медведь** (bear)
m'ehd-V'EHD'

2) **гиена** (hyena)
g'i-JEH-na

3) **шакал** (jackal)
sha-KAL

4) **корова** (cow)
ka-RO-va

5) **бык** (bull)
byk

6) **лиса** (fox)
l'i-SA

7) **буйвол** (buffalo)
BUJ-vəl

8) **лось** (elk/moose)
los'

9) **овца** (sheep)
av-TSA

10) **коза** (goat)
ka-ZA

11) **газель** (gazelle)
ga-ZEHL'

12) **волк** (wolf)
volk

13) **обезьяна** (monkey)
a-b'ehz'-JA-na

14) **баран** (ram)
ba-RAN

15) **осёл** (donkey)
a-S'OL

А вы знали, что медведь может быстро бегать?
Did you know that the bear can run fast?

Волки часто нападают на овец.
Wolves often attack sheep.

Коровы и козы дают людям молоко.
Cows and goats give people milk.

РЫБЫ И МОЛЛЮСКИ (FISH AND MOLLUSKS)

- **Рыбы (Fish)**
  RY-by

1) **китовая акула** (whale shark)
   k'i-TO-va-ja a-KU-la

2) **белая акула** (white shark)
   B'EH-la-ja a-KU-la

3) **акула-молот** (hammerhead shark)
   a-KU-la-MO-lət

4) **рыба-меч** (swordfish/marlin)
   RY-ba-m'ehch

5) **барракуда** (barracuda)
   ba-ra-KU-da

6) **рыба фугу** (pufferfish)
   RY-ba FU-gu

7) **сом** (catfish)
   som

8) **пиранья** (piranha)
   p'i-RAN'-JA

9) **летучая рыба** (flying fish)
   l'eh-TU-cha-ja RY-ba

10) **мурена** (moray eel)
    mu-R'EH-na

11) **скат манта** (manta ray)
    skat MAN-ta

12) **морской конёк** (seahorse)
    mar-SKOJ ka-N'OK

- **Моллюски (Mollusks)**
  ma-L'U-sk'i

13) **кальмар** (squid)
    kal'-MAR

14) **каракатица** (cuttlefish)
    ka-ra-KA-t'i-tsa

15) **осьминог** (octopus)
    as'-m'i-NOH

16) **устрица** (oyster)
    U-st'ri-tsa

17) **двустворчатый моллюск** (clam)
    dvu-STVOR-cha-tyj ma-L'USK

18) **наутилус** (nautilus)
    na-u-T'I-lus

19) **улитка** (snail)
    u-L'IT-ka

20) **слизняк** (slug)
    sl'iz-N'AK

Морские коньки такие милые!
Seahorses are so cute!

Осьминоги могут быть как крошечными, так и огромными.
Octopuses can be both tiny and huge.

Пираний привлекает запах крови.
Piranhas are attracted by the smell of blood.

ОДЕЖДА I (CLOTHING I)

1) **плащ** (raincoat)
   plasch

2) **кофта с капюшоном** (hoodie)
   KOF-ta s ka-p'u-SHO-nəm

3) **куртка** (jacket)
   KUR-tka

4) **джинсы** (jeans)
   DZHYN-sy

5) **трусы-боксеры** (boxer shorts)
   tru-SY-BOK-s'eh-ry

6) **ботинки** (boots)
   ba-T'IN-k'i

7) **серёжки** (earrings)
   s'eh-R'OZH-k'i

8) **свитер** (sweater)
   SV'I-tehr

9) **колье** (necklace)
   kal'-JEH

10) **бюстгальтер** (bra)
    b'ust-GAL'-t'ehr

11) **леггинсы** (leggings)
    L'EH-g'in-sy

12) **носки** (socks)
    nas-K'I

13) **блузка/топ** (blouse/top)
    BLUZ-ka/top

14) **браслет** (bracelet)
    bras-L'EHT

15) **шорты** (shorts)
    SHOR-ty

16) **трусики** (panties)
    TRU-s'i-k'i

17) **пальто** (coat)
    pal'-TO

18) **платье** (dress)
    PLA-t'jeh

19) **сумочка** (purse)
    SU-mach-ka

20) **сандали** (sandals)
    san-DAL'-i

Я не ношу браслеты и серёжки.
I don't wear bracelets and earrings.

Кто-нибудь видел мою коричневую куртку?
Has anybody seen my brown jacket?

Моя племянница терпеть не может платья.
My niece can't stand dresses.

ОДЕЖДА II (CLOTHING II)

1) **шляпа** (hat)
SHL'A-pa

2) **смокинг** (tuxedo/smoking)
SMO-k'ing

3) **галстук-бабочка** (bow tie)
GAL-stuk-BA-ba-chka

4) **обувь** (shoes)
O-buf'

5) **костюм** (suit)
kas-T'UM

6) **рубашка** (shirt)
ru-BASH-ka

7) **галстук** (tie)
GAL-stuk

8) **кейс** (briefcase/case)
k'ehjs

9) **кофта с длинными рукавами**
(long-sleeved blouse)
KOF-ta s DL'IN-ny-m'i ru-ka-VA-m'i

10) **спортивный бюстгалтер** (sports
bra)
spar-T'IV-nyj b'ust-GAL-t'ehr

11) **брюки/штаны** (trousers/pants)
BR'U-k'i/shta-NY

12) **ремень** (belt)
r'eh-M'EN'

13) **кольцо** (ring)
kal'-TSO

14) **футболка** (T-shirt)
fut-BOL-ka

15) **юбка** (skirt)
JU-pka

16) **шарф** (scarf)
sharf

17) **часы** (watch)
cha-SY

18) **штаны с карманами** (cargo pants)
shta-NY s kar-MA-na-m'i

19) **бумажник** (wallet)
bu-MAZH-n'ik

20) **зонт** (umbrella)
zont

Этот ремень слишком длинный для моих брюк.
This belt is too long for my trousers.

Я хочу, чтобы зонт подходил к шляпе по цвету.
I want the umbrella to match the hat in color.

Обувь должна быть удобной.
Shoes must be comfortable.

ПОГОДА (THE WEATHER)

1) **солнечно** (sunny)
SOL-n'ehch-nə

2) **жарко** (hot)
ZHAR-kə

3) **песчаная буря** (sandstorm)
p'eh-SCHA-na-ja BU-r'a

4) **облачно** (cloudy)
O-blach-nə

5) **тепло** (warm)
t'ehp-LO

6) **туманно** (foggy/misty)
tu-MAN-nə

7) **дождливо** (rainy)
dazh-DL'I-və

8) **прохладно** (cool)
prah-LAD-nə

9) **капля дождя** (raindrop)
KAP-l'a dazh-D'A

10) **влажно** (humid)
VLAZH-nə

11) **буря** (storm)
BU-r'a

12) **молния** (lightning)
MOL-n'i-ja

13) **ветрено** (windy)
V'EH-tr'eh-nə

14) **снежно** (snowy)
SN'EH-zhnə

15) **холодно** (cold)
HO-ləd-nə

16) **снежинка** (snowflake)
sn'eh-ZHYN-ka

Каждая снежинка имеет уникальную форму.
Every snowflake has a unique shape.

Сегодня так жарко!
It's so hot today!

На улице сегодня очень ветрено.
It's very windy outside today.

ВРЕМЕНА ГОДА: ВЕСНА (THE SEASONS – SPRING)

1) **сад** (garden)
sat

2) **цветок** (blossom)
tsv'eh-TOK

3) **пикник** (picnic)
p'ik-N'IK

4) **парк** (park)
park

5) **поездка на велосипеде** (bike ride)
pa-JEHZ-tka na v'eh-la-s'i-P'EH-d'eh

6) **лимонад** (lemonade)
l'i-ma-NAT

7) **гаражная распродажа** (garage sale)
ga-RAZH-na-ja ras-pra-DA-zha

8) **поездка на автомобиле** (road trip)
pa-JEZ-tka na af-ta-ma-B'I-l'eh

9) **красить камни** (to paint rocks)
KRA-s'it' KAM-n'i

10) **сажать цветы** (to plant some flowers)
sa-ZHAT' tsv'eh-ty

11) **запускать воздушного змея** (to fly a kite)
za-pus-KAT' vaz-DUSH-nə-və ZM'EH-ja

12) **идти на шашлыки** (to attend a barbecue)
i-T'I na shash-ly-K'I

На улице был небольшой ветер, и мы запускали воздушного змея.
It was a bit windy outside and we flew a kite.

Наш парк прекрасен весной.
Our park is wonderful in spring.

Весной у меня много работы в саду.
In spring I've got a lot to do in the garden.

ВРЕМЕНА ГОДА: ЛЕТО (THE SEASONS – SUMMER)

1) **жить в палатках** (to go camping)
zhyt' v pa-LAT-kah

2) **аквапарк** (water park)
akva-PARK

3) **игры на свежем воздухе** (outdoor activities)
IG-ry na SV'EH-zhehm VOZ-du-h'eh

4) **бассейн** (swimming pool)
ba-S'EHJN

5) **плавать** (to swim)
PLA-vat'

6) **загорать** (to get tanned)
za-ga-RAT'

7) **крем от солнца** (sunscreen)
kr'ehm at SON-tsa

8) **спрей от насекомых** (insect repellent)
sprehj at na-s'eh-KO-myh

9) **озеро** (lake)
O-z'eh-ra

10) **пляжный спасатель** (lifesaver/lifeguard)
PL'AZH-nyj spa-SA-t'ehl'

11) **замок из песка** (sandcastle)
ZA-mək iz p'ehs-KA

12) **идти в поход** (to go on a hike)
i-T'I v pa-HOT

Мне больше нравится плавать в озере, чем в бассейне.
I prefer swimming in a lake over a swimming pool.

Не забудь взять крем от солнца, когда пойдёшь на пляж.
Don't forget to take a sunscreen when you go to the beach.

Летом он работает спасателем.
He works as a lifeguard in summer.

QUIZ #2

Use arrows to match the corresponding translations:

a. swim

b. wallet

c. crocodile

d. blossom

e. cold

f. rat

g. dress

h. bear

i. to get tanned

j. spider

k. sunny

l. snail

m. squirrel

n. jacket

o. monkey

p. butterfly

1. крокодил

2. бабочка

3. паук

4. крыса

5. белка

6. обезьяна

7. медведь

8. улитка

9. куртка

10. платье

11. бумажник

12. холодно

13. цветок

14. плавать

15. загорать

16. солнечно

Fill in the blank spaces with the options below (use each word only once):

Мои друзья хотят _____ на этих выходных. Они говорят, что это будет весело. Но мне не нравится эта идея. Палатки – это дискомфорт. Нужно брать с собой шорты, джинсы, плащи, а я люблю платья и _____. Будет солнечно и жарко, а я не люблю такую погоду. Я люблю, когда _____. Да, там будет _____, но я не люблю плавать. Я могу загорать, когда есть _____, но недолго. Плюс я боюсь насекомых: слепни, мухи, _____! А дикие животные? Летучие мыши и _____! А ещё мои друзья будут есть _____ из озера. Но я не люблю рыбу! Наверное, я останусь дома.

озеро   прохладно

юбки   крем от солнца

комары   жить в палатках

волки   рыбу

ВРЕМЕНА ГОДА: ОСЕНЬ (THE SEASONS – FALL/AUTUMN)

1) **опавшая листва** (fallen leaves)
a-PAF-sha-ja l'is-TVA

2) **убирать листья** (to rake leaves)
u-b'i-RAT' L'IS-t'ja

3) **тыква** (pumpkin)
TYK-va

4) **вырезать тыкву** (to carve a pumpkin)
vy-r'eh-ZAT' TYK-vu

5) **сбор яблок** (apple picking)
zbor JAB-lək

6) **костюм на Хэллоуин** (Halloween costume)
kas-t'um na HEH-lo-u-in

7) **конфеты на Хэллоуин** (Halloween candy)
kan-F'EH-ty na HEH-lo-u-in

8) **ароматические свечи** (scented candles)
a-ra-ma-T'I-ch'ehs-k'i-jeh SV'EH-chi

9) **ужин на день Благодарения** (Thanksgiving dinner)
U-zhyn na d'ehn' bla-ga-da-R'EH-n'i-ja

10) **шерстяной плед** (wool blanket)
sh'her-st'a-NOJ pl'eht

11) **жарить зефирки** (to roast marshmallows)
ZHA-r'it' z'eh-F'IR-k'i

12) **украшать сад** (to decorate the garden)
uk-ra-SHAT' sat

Собирать листья в саду осенью – это обязанность наших детей.
Raking leaves in the garden in autumn is our kids' duty.

Мы купили ароматические свечи для холодных осенних вечеров.
We bought scented candles for cold autumn nights.

Я подарю бабушке тёплый шерстяной плед.
I'll give my grandmother a warm wool blanket as a present.

ВРЕМЕНА ГОДА: ЗИМА (THE SEASONS – WINTER)

1) **горячий шоколад** (hot cocoa/hot chocolate)
ga-R'A-chij sha-ka-LAT

2) **санки** (sled)
SAN-k'i

3) **варежки** (mittens)
VA-r'ehzh-k'i

4) **дутая куртка** (puffy jacket)
DU-ta-ja KUR-tka

5) **суп** (soup)
sup

6) **имбирное печенье** (gingerbread cookies)
im-B'IR-nə-jeh p'eh-CHEH-n'jeh

7) **замёрзшее окно** (frosty window)
za-M'OR-sheh-jeh ak-NO

8) **сосновая шишка** (pinecone)
sas-NO-və-j'a SHY-shka

9) **катание на коньках** (ice skating)
ka-TA-n'i-jeh na kan'-KAH

10) **кататься на лыжах** (ski)
ka-TA-tsa na LY-zhah

11) **каток** (ice rink)
ka-TOK

12) **снежок** (snowball)
sn'eh-ZHOK

Бабушка связала мне новые варежки.
Grandmother has knitted new mittens for me.

Чашка горячего шоколада – мой любимый зимний десерт.
A cup of hot chocolate is my favorite winter dessert.

Пора доставать из шкафа свою дутую куртку.
It's time to take my puffy jacket out of the closet.

ВРЕМЯ (TIME)

1) **часовой пояс** (time zone)
cha-sa-VOJ PO-jas

2) **секунда** (second)
s'eh-KUN-da

3) **минута** (minute)
m'i-NU-ta

4) **час** (hour)
chas

5) **день** (day)
d'ehn'

6) **неделя** (week)
n'eh-D'EH-l'a

7) **две недели** (fortnight)
dv'eh n'eh-D'EH-l'i

8) **месяц** (month)
M'EH-s'ats

9) **год** (year)
got

10) **рассвет** (dawn)
ras-SV'EHT

11) **утро** (morning)
U-tra

12) **полдень** (noon/midday)
POL-d'ehn'

13) **день** (afternoon)
d'ehn'

14) **сумерки** (dusk)
SU-m'ehr-k'i

15) **ночь** (night)
noch

16) **полночь** (midnight)
POL-nəch

17) **дата** (date)
DA-ta

18) **календарь** (calendar)
ka-l'ehn-DAR'

Год закончился, и мне нужно купить новый календарь.
The year is over and I need to buy a new calendar.

Ты свободна через час?
Will you be free in an hour?

Полночь – это волшебное время в сказках.
Midnight is magic time in fairy tales.

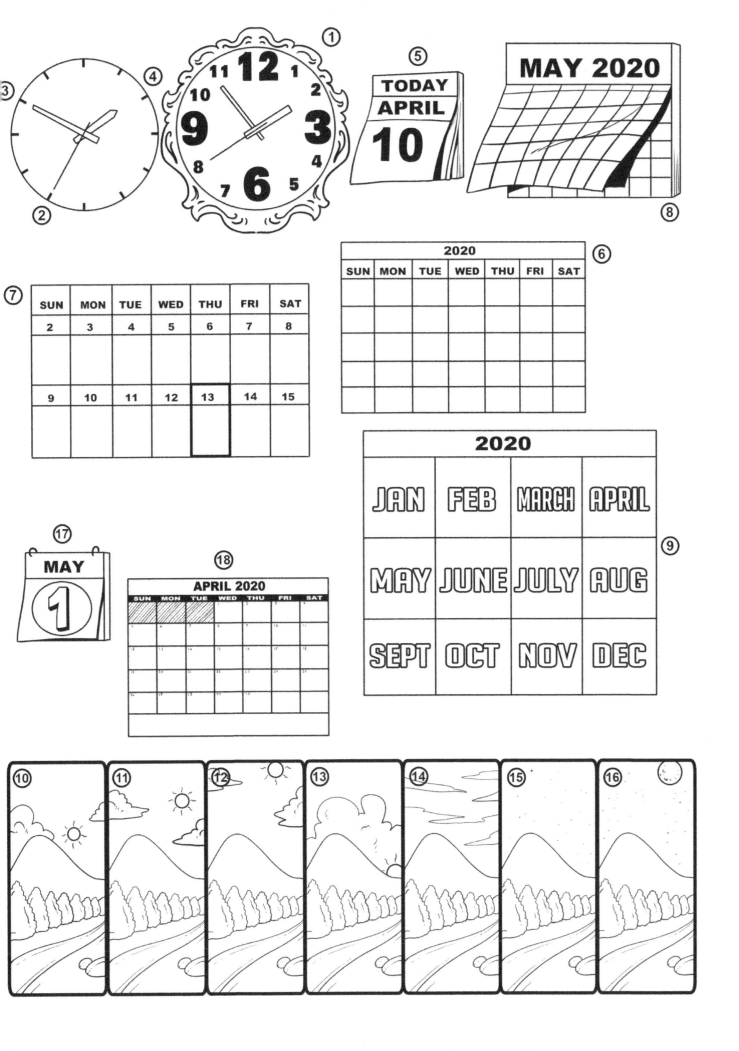

ДОМ (THE HOUSE)

1) **чердак** (attic)
   chehr-DAK

2) **крыша** (roof)
   KRY-sha

3) **потолок** (ceiling)
   pa-ta-LOK

4) **труба** (chimney)
   tru-BA

5) **стена** (wall)
   st'eh-NA

6) **балкон** (balcony)
   bal-KON

7) **крыльцо** (porch)
   kryl'-TSO

8) **окно** (window)
   ak-NO

9) **жалюзи** (shutters)
   ZHA-l'u-z'i

10) **дверь** (door)
    dv'ehr'

11) **лестница** (stairs)
    L'EHS-n'i-tsa

12) **перила** (banister)
    p'eh-R'I-la

13) **пол** (floor)
    pol

14) **подвал** (basement)
    pad-VAL

15) **задний двор** (backyard)
    ZAD-n'ij dvor

16) **гараж** (garage)
    ga-RAZH

17) **въезд** (driveway)
    vjehst

18) **забор** (fence/picket fence)
    za-BOR

19) **почтовый ящик** (mailbox)
    pach-TO-vyj JA-schik

20) **коридор** (hallway/corridor)
    ka-r'i-DOR

В детстве мы верили, что на чердаке живут привидения.
In our childhood, we used to believe that there were ghosts living in the attic.

Задний двор наших соседей такой грязный!
Our neighbors' backyard is so dirty!

Наши перила сломались, и нам нужны новые.
Our banister is broken and we need a new one.

ПРЕДМЕТЫ НА КУХНЕ (KITCHEN ITEMS)

1) **плита** (stove)
   pl'i-TA

2) **микроволновка** (microwave oven)
   m'ik-ra-val-NOF-ka

3) **духовка** (oven)
   du-HOF-ka

4) **электрический миксер** (electric mixer)
   eh-l'ehk-TR'I-ches-k'ij M'IK-s'ehr

5) **блендер** (blender)
   BLEHN-dehr

6) **тостер** (toaster oven)
   TOS-tehr

7) **кофеварка** (coffee maker)
   ko-f'eh-VAR-ka

8) **холодильник** (fridge)
   ha-la-D'IL'-n'ik

9) **кладовая** (pantry)
   kla-da-VA-ja

10) **шкафчик** (cupboard)
    SHKAF-chik

11) **форма для выпечки** (cake pan)
    FOR-ma dl'a VY-p'ehch-k'i

12) **сковорода** (frying pan)
    ska-va-ra-DA

13) **кастрюля** (pot)
    kas-TR'U-l'a

14) **формочки для печенья** (cookie cutters)
    FOR-mach-k'i dl'a p'eh-CHEHN'-ja

15) **миска** (mixing bowl)
    M'IS-ka

16) **дуршлаг** (colander)
    dur-SHLAG

17) **сито** (strainer)
    S'I-tə

18) **скалка** (rolling pin)
    SKAL-ka

19) **прихватка** (oven mitt)
    pr'ih-VAT-ka

20) **передник/фартук** (apron)
    p'eh-R'EHD-n'ik/FAR-tuk

Ты не приготовишь этот крем без электрического миксера.
You won't cook this cream without an electric mixer.

Холодильник совсем пустой. Пора идти за покупками!
The fridge is totally empty. It's time to go shopping!

Твоя кладовая похожа на магазин: здесь есть всё!
Your pantry looks like a shop: you've got everything here!

ПРЕДМЕТЫ В СПАЛЬНЕ (BEDROOM ITEMS)

1) **кровать** (bed)
   kra-VAT′

2) **матрас** (mattress)
   mat-RAS

3) **постельное бельё** (bedding/bed linen)
   pas-T′EHL-nə-jeh b′ehl′-JO

4) **подушка** (pillow)
   pa-DUSH-ka

5) **простыня** (sheets)
   pras-TY-n′a

6) **покрывало** (blanket)
   pak-ry-VA-lə

7) **наматрасник** (spread)
   na-mat-RAS-n′ik

8) **наволочка** (pillowcase)
   na-va-LACH-ka

9) **прикроватная тумбочка** (nightstand)
   pr′i-kra-VAT-nə-ja TUM-bəch-ka

10) **часы** (table clock)
    cha-SY

11) **настольная лампа** (table lamp)
    nas-TOL′-nə-ja LAM-pa

12) **шкаф** (closet)
    shkaf

13) **кресло-качалка** (rocking chair)
    KR′EHS-lə ka-CHAL-ka

14) **лампа** (lamp)
    LAM-pa

15) **зеркало** (mirror)
    Z′HER-kə-lə

16) **комод** (dresser)
    ka-MOT

17) **штора** (curtain)
    SHTO-ra

18) **колыбель** (cradle/crib)
    ka-ly-B′EHL′

19) **игрушки над колыбелью** (crib mobile)
    ig-RUSH-ki nat ka-ly-B′EHL′ju

20) **вешалка** (hanger)
    V′EH-shal-ka

Кресло-качалка занимает слишком много места в этой комнате.
The rocking chair takes up too much space in this room.

Чистое и свежее постельное бельё – это маленькая радость жизни.
Clean and fresh bed linen is a little pleasure of life.

Эта вешалка очень удобная.
This hanger is very convenient.

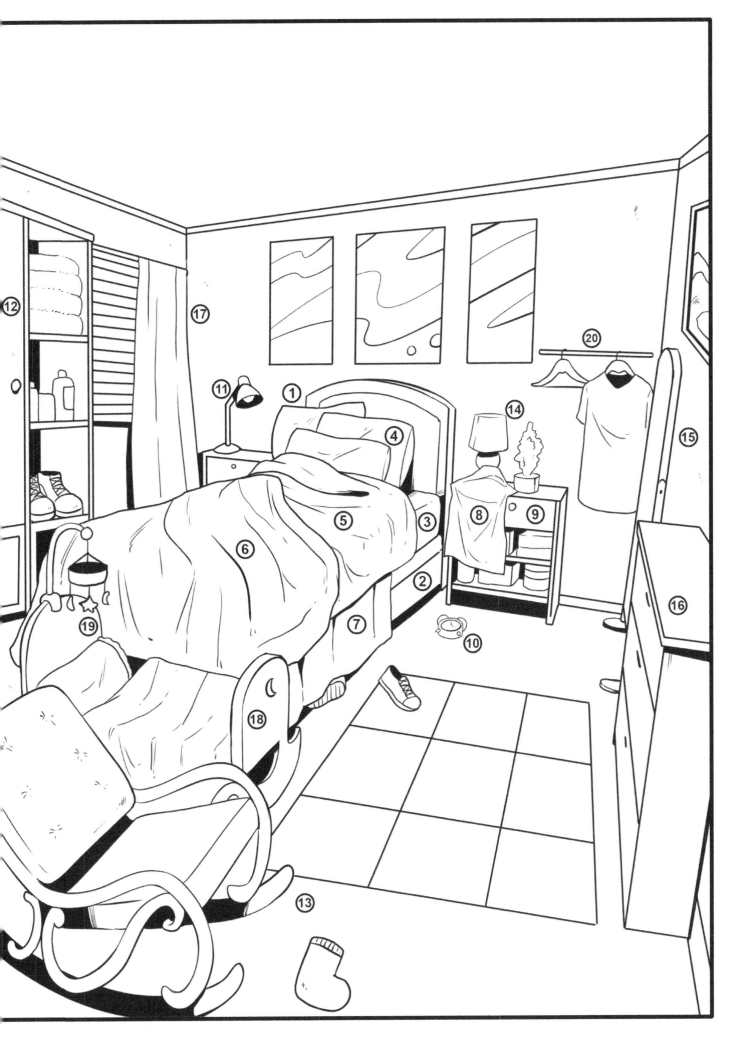

ПРЕДМЕТЫ В ВАННОЙ (BATHROOM ITEMS)

1) **шторка для душа** (shower curtain)
   SHTOR-ka dl'a DU-sha

2) **полотенце** (towel)
   pa-la-T'EHN-tseh

3) **вешалка для полотенец** (towel rack)
   V'EH-shal-ka dl'a pa-la-T'EH-n'ehts

4) **полотенце для рук** (hand towel)
   pa-la-T'EHN-tseh dl'a ruk

5) **ванна** (bathtub)
   VAN-na

6) **душ** (shower)
   dush

7) **туалет** (toilet/WC)
   tu-a-L'EHT

8) **раковина** (sink/washbasin)
   RA-ka-v'i-na

9) **кран** (faucet/tap)
   kran

10) **коврик для ванной** (bathmat)
    KOV-r'ik dl'a VAN-nəj

11) **аптечка** (medicine cabinet)
    ap-T'EH-chka

12) **зубная паста** (toothpaste)
    zub-NA-ja PAS-ta

13) **зубная щётка** (toothbrush)
    zub-NA-ja SCHO-tka

14) **шампунь** (shampoo)
    sham-PUN'

15) **расчёска** (comb)
    ras-CHOS-ka

16) **мыло** (soap)
    MY-lə

17) **пена для бритья** (shaving foam)
    P'EH-na dl'a br'i-T'JA

18) **бритва** (razor/shaver)
    BR'I-tva

19) **туалетная бумага** (toilet paper)
    tu-a-L'EHT-na-ja bu-MA-ga

20) **вантуз** (plunger)
    VAN-tuz

21) **ёршик для унитаза** (toilet brush)
    JOR-shik dl'a u-n'i-TA-za

22) **корзина для мусора** (wastebasket)
    kar-Z'I-na dl'a MU-sə-ra

Кто снова взял моё полотенце?
Who took my towel again?

Я не знаю, как пользоваться вантузом.
I don't know how to use a plunger.

У тебя такая чистая ванна. Каким средством ты пользуешься?
Your bathtub is so clean. What detergent do you use?

ПРЕДМЕТЫ В ГОСТИНОЙ (LIVING ROOM ITEMS)

1) **мебель** (furniture)
M'EH-b'ehl'

2) **стул** (chair)
stul

3) **диван** (sofa)
d'i-VAN

4) **кушетка** (couch)
ku-SHEH-tka

5) **подушка** (cushion)
pa-DUSH-ka

6) **кофейный столик** (coffee table)
ka-F'EHJ-nyj STO-l'ik

7) **пепельница** (ashtray)
P'EH-p'ehl'-n'i-tsa

8) **ваза** (vase)
VA-za

9) **украшения** (decorations)
uk-ra-SHEH-n'i-ja

10) **книжная полка**
(bookshelf/bookcase)
KN'I-zhna-ja POL-ka

11) **подставка для журналов** (magazine holder)
pat-STAF-ka dl'a zhur-NA-ləf

12) **стерео** (stereo)
ST'EH-r'eh-ə

13) **колонки** (speakers)
ka-LON-k'i

14) **камин** (fireplace)
ka-M'IN

15) **люстра** (chandelier)
L'US-tra

16) **лампа** (lamp)
LAM-pa

17) **лампочка** (light bulb)
LAM-pəch-ka

18) **настенные часы** (wall clock)
nas-T'EHN-ny-jeh cha-SY

19) **картина** (painting)
kar-T'I-na

20) **телевизор** (TV/television)
t'eh-l'eh-V'I-zər

21) **пульт** (remote control)
pul't

22) **игровая приставка** (video game console)
ig-ra-VA-j'a pr'is-TAF-ka

Вся мебель в этой комнате старинная и дорогая.
All the furniture in this room is ancient and expensive.

Нужно поменять лампочку в люстре.
We need to change the light bulb in the chandelier.

Эти подушки такие мягкие! Я могу провести на них весь день.
These cushions are so soft! I can spend all day on them.

ПРЕДМЕТЫ В СТОЛОВОЙ (DINING ROOM ITEMS)

1) **обеденный стол** (dining table)
a-B'EH-d'ehn-nyj stol

2) **скатерть** (tablecloth)
SKA-t'ehrt'

3) **центр стола** (centerpiece)
tsehntr sta-LA

4) **салфетка под прибор** (placemat)
sal-F'EH-tka pat pr'i-BOR

5) **тарелка** (plate)
ta-R'EHL-ka

6) **салфетка** (napkin)
sal-F'EH-tka

7) **нож** (knife)
nosh

8) **вилка** (fork)
V'IL-ka

9) **ложка** (spoon)
LOZH-ka

10) **кувшин** (pitcher/jar)
kuf-SHYN

11) **стакан** (glass)
sta-KAN

12) **кружка/чашка** (mug/cup)
KRUSH-ka/CHASH-ka

13) **солонка** (saltshaker)
sa-LON-ka

14) **перечница** (pepper shaker)
P'EH-r'ehch-n'i-tsa

15) **поднос** (tray)
pad-NOS

16) **напиток** (drink/beverage)
na-P'I-tək

17) **еда** (food)
jeh-DA

18) **закуска** (snack)
za-KUS-ka

Закуски мне нравятся даже больше, чем основные блюда.
I like snacks even more than main courses.

Передай мне солонку, пожалуйста.
Could you give me the saltshaker, please?

Что у тебя в стакане?
What's in your glass?

QUIZ #3

Use arrows to match the corresponding translations:

a. sink

b. ashtray

c. oven

d. morning

e. tablecloth

f. pillow

g. week

h. fallen leaves

i. painting

j. bowl

k. pepper shaker

l. closet

m. porch

n. sledge

o. toothpaste

p. soup

1. утро

2. неделя

3. шкаф

4. подушка

5. раковина

6. зубная паста

7. пепельница

8. санки

9. миска

10. перечница

11. крыльцо

12. духовка

13. картина

14. скатерть

15. суп

16. опавшая листва

Fill in the blank spaces with the options below (use each word only once):

Этот _____ самый счастливый в моей жизни: мы купили дом! Мы переезжаем через _____. Возле дома есть большой _____ для нашей машины. Перед домом большое _____. Здесь я буду укрываться шерстяным пледом и читать книги. Откроем _____? Гостиная большая, мне очень нравится диван и _____. И, конечно же, _____ для моих книг! В кухне есть большая _____ и духовка. Здесь я буду печь _____. В столовой большой и широкий _____ – как раз для нашей семьи. В спальне есть кровать и _____, но он маленький для моих вещей. В ванной есть _____, но нет ванны. Я очень счастлива и не могу дождаться переезда!

две недели	дверь
камин	год
обеденный стол	имбирное печенье
кладовая	книжная полка
крыльцо	душ
комод	гараж

САД (THE GARDEN/THE BACKYARD)

1) **садовник** (gardener)
   sa-DOV-n'ik

2) **сарай** (shed)
   SA-raj

3) **куст** (bush)
   kust

4) **газон** (lawn)
   ga-ZON

5) **трава** (grass)
   tra-VA

6) **цветок** (flower)
   tsv'eh-TOK

7) **садовый шланг** (garden hose)
   sa-DO-vyj shlank

8) **лейка** (watering can)
   L'EHJ-ka

9) **цветочный горшок** (flowerpot)
   tsv'eh-TOCH-nyj gar-SHOK

10) **садовые перчатки** (gardening gloves)
    sa-DO-vy-jeh p'her-CHAT-k'i

11) **лопата** (shovel)
    la-PA-ta

12) **грабли** (rake)
    GRAB-l'i

13) **вилы** (gardening fork)
    V'I-ly

14) **секатор** (pruners/pruning shears)
    s'eh-KA-tər

15) **садовая лопатка** (garden trowel)
    sa-DO-va-ja la-PAT-ka

16) **кран** (tap)
    kran

17) **тачка** (wheelbarrow)
    TA-chka

18) **газонокосилка** (lawn mower)
    ga-zo-na-ka-S'IL-ka

19) **фонарик** (lantern)
    fa-NA-r'ik

20) **лоза** (vine)
    la-ZA

Принеси лейку из сарая, пожалуйста.
Could you bring the watering can from the shed please?

Он может целый день работать в саду.
He can work in the garden all day long.

Почему ты работаешь без садовых перчаток?
Why are you working without your gardening gloves?

УБОРКА (THE CLEANING ROOM)

1) **стиральная машина** (washing machine)
st'i-RAL'-na-ja ma-SHY-na

2) **сушилка** (dryer)
su-SHYL-ka

3) **утюг** (iron)
u-T'UH

4) **гладильная доска** (ironing board)
gla-D'IL'-na-ja das-KA

5) **хозяйственное мыло** (laundry soap)
ha-Z'AJ-stv'eh-nə-jeh MY-lə

6) **стиральный порошок** (laundry detergent)
st'i-RAL'-nyj pa-ra-SHOK

7) **кондиционер** (fabric softener)
kan-d'i-tsy-a-N'ER

8) **корзина для белья** (laundry basket)
kar-Z'I-na dl'a b'ehl'-JA

9) **грязное бельё** (dirty clothes)
GR'AZ-nə-jeh b'ehl'-JO

10) **чистое бельё** (clean laundry)
CHIS-tə-jeh b'ehl'-JO

11) **метла** (broom)
m'eht-LA

12) **совок** (dust pan)
sa-VOK

13) **резиновые перчатки** (rubber gloves)
r'eh-Z'I-nə-vy-jeh p'ehr-CHAT-k'i

14) **губка** (sponge)
GUP-ka

15) **таз** (plastic tub)
tas

16) **швабра** (mop)
SHVAB-ra

17) **ведро** (bucket)
v'ehd-RO

18) **тряпочки** (cleaning cloths)
TR'A-pəch-k'i

19) **щётка** (scrub brush)
SCHOT-ka

20) **отбеливатель** (bleach)
at-B'EH-l'i-va-t'ehl'

21) **дезинфектор** (disinfectant)
d'ehz-in-F'EHK-tər

22) **мусорное ведро** (trash can)
MU-sər-nə-jeh v'ehd-RO

Корзина для белья снова полная.
The laundry basket is full again.

Отбеливатель может испортить одежду.
A bleach can ruin clothes.

Ты пользуешься кондиционером?
Do you use a fabric softener?

ШКОЛА/УНИВЕРСИТЕТ (THE SCHOOL/THE UNIVERSITY)

1) **учитель** (teacher)
u-CHI-t'ehl'

2) **ученик/студент** (student)
u-cheh-N'IK/stu-D'EHNT

3) **класс** (classroom)
klas

4) **шкафчик** (locker)
SHKAF-chik

5) **доска объявлений** (bulletin board)
das-KA ab-jav-L'EH-n'ij

6) **листок бумаги** (sheet of paper)
l'is-TOK bu-MA-g'i

7) **книга** (book)
KN'I-ga

8) **блокнот** (notebook)
blak-NOT

9) **клей** (glue)
kl'ehj

10) **ножницы** (scissors)
NOZH-n'i-tsy

11) **карандаш** (pencil)
ka-ran-DASH

12) **ластик** (eraser)
LAS-t'ik

13) **точилка** (pencil sharpener)
ta-CHIL-ka

14) **ручка** (pen)
RUCH-ka

15) **маркер** (marker)
MAR-k'ehr

16) **хайлайтер** (highlighter)
haj-LAJ-ter

17) **конверт** (envelope)
kan-V'EHRT

18) **папка-планшет** (clipboard)
PAP-ka-plan-SHEHT

19) **доска** (blackboard)
das-KA

20) **калькулятор** (calculator)
kal'-ku-L'A-tər

21) **линейка** (ruler)
l'i-N'EHJ-ka

22) **стэплер** (stapler)
STEHP-l'ehr

23) **пенал** (pouch/pencil case)
p'eh-NAL

24) **школьная парта** (school desk)
SHKOL'-na-ja PAR-ta

25) **стол** (table)
stol

26) **ноутбук** (laptop)
no-ud-BUK

Ты видела список учеников на доске объявлений?
Did you see the list of students on the bulletin board?

Я не пользуюсь калькулятором на уроке математики.
I don't use a calculator at math classes.

Дети, это ваш новый учитель физики.
Kids, this is your new physics teacher.

ОФИС (THE OFFICE)

1) **начальник** (boss)
na-CHAL'-n'ik

2) **руководитель** (head)
ru-ka-va-D'I-t'ehl'

3) **работник** (employee)
ra-BOT-n'ik

4) **директор** (CEO/president)
d'i-R'EHK-tər

5) **бизнес-партнёр** (business partner)
B'IZ-nehs-par-TN'OR

6) **коллега** (colleague)
ka-L'EH-ga

7) **сотрудник/сотрудница** (co-worker m./f.)
sa-TRUD-n'ik/sa-TRUD-n'i-tsa

8) **секретарь** (secretary)
s'eh-kr'eh-TAR'

9) **кабинет** (cubicle)
ka-b'i-N'ET

10) **вращающийся стул** (swivel chair)
vra-SCHA-ju-schij-s'a stul

11) **рабочий стол** (desk)
ra-BO-chij stol

12) **компьютер** (computer)
kam-P'U-təhr

13) **принтер** (printer)
PR'IN-tər

14) **канцелярские принадлежности** (office supplies)
kan-tseh-L'AR-sk'i-jeh p'ri-nad-L'EHZH-nəs-t'i

15) **печать** (rubber stamp)
p'eh-CHAT'

16) **диспенсер для скотча** (tape dispenser)
d'is-PEHN-s'ehr dl'a SKO-tcha

17) **папка** (folder)
PAP-ka

18) **шкаф для бумаг** (filing cabinet)
shkaf dl'a bu-MAH

19) **факс** (fax)
faks

20) **телефон** (telephone)
t'eh-l'eh-FON

Наш начальник очень понимающий человек.
Our boss is a very understanding man.

Она работает секретарём в большой компании.
She works as a secretary in a big company.

Его рабочий стол всегда в беспорядке!
His desk is always a mess!

ПРОФЕССИИ (PROFESSIONS/OCCUPATIONS)

1) **инженер** (engineer)
   in-zheh-N'ER

2) **космонавт** (astronaut)
   kas-ma-NAFT

3) **пилот** (pilot)
   p'i-LOT

4) **судья** (judge)
   su-D'JA

5) **пожарный** (firefighter)
   pa-ZHAR-nyj

6) **полицейский** (police officer)
   pa-l'i-TSEHJ-sk'ij

7) **повар** (chef)
   PO-var

8) **дирижёр** (conductor)
   d'i-r'i-ZHOR

9) **профессор** (professor)
   pra-F'EH-sər

10) **танцор/танцовщица** (dancer)
    tan-TSOR/tan-TSOF-schi-tsa

11) **бизнесмен** (businessman)
    b'iz-nehs-MEHN

12) **дрессировщик** (animal trainer)
    d'reh-s'i-ROF-schik

Многие дети мечтают стать космонавтами.
Many kids dream of being astronauts.

Судья был несправедлив.
The judge was unfair.

Я много тренировался, чтобы стать пилотом.
I trained a lot to become a pilot.

ВИДЫ ТРАНСПОРТА (MEANS OF TRANSPORT)

1) **велосипед** (bike/bicycle)
   v'eh-la-s'i-P'EHT

2) **мотоцикл** (motorcycle/motorbike)
   ma-ta-TSYKL

3) **снегоход** (snowmobile)
   sn'eh-ga-HOT

4) **машина** (car/automobile)
   ma-SHY-na

5) **автобус** (bus)
   af-TO-bus

6) **грузовик** (truck)
   gru-za-V'IK

7) **метро** (subway)
   m'eh-TRO

8) **поезд** (train)
   PO-jehst

9) **гидроцикл** (jet ski)
   g'idra-TSYKL

10) **лодка** (boat)
    LOT-ka

11) **круизный лайнер** (cruise ship)
    kru-IZ-nyj LAJ-n'ehr

12) **подводная лодка** (submarine)
    pad-VOD-na-ja LOT-ka

13) **дирижабль** (airship/blimp)
    d'i-r'i-ZHABL'

14) **воздушный шар** (hot air balloon)
    vaz-DUSH-nyj shar

15) **самолёт** (plane/airplane)
    sa-ma-L'OT

16) **вертолёт** (helicopter/chopper)
    v'her-ta-L'OT

17) **космический шаттл** (space shuttle)
    kas-M'I-chehs-k'ij shatl

Вы поедете на поезде или на машине?
Will you go by train or by car?

Мы выиграли путешествие на круизном лайнере.
We've won a trip on a cruise ship.

Мой дедушка водит грузовик.
My grandfather drives a truck.

ПЕЙЗАЖИ (LANDSCAPES)

1) **гора** (mountain)
   ga-RA

2) **тропический лес** (tropical rainforest)
   tra-P'I-chehs-k'ij l'ehs

3) **пустыня** (desert)
   pus-TY-n'a

4) **вулкан** (volcano)
   vul-KAN

5) **скала** (cliff)
   ska-LA

6) **пляж** (beach)
   pl'azh

7) **лес** (forest)
   l'ehs

8) **пещера** (cave)
   p'eh-SCHEH-ra

9) **гейзер** (geyser)
   G'EHJ-z'ehr

10) **водопад** (waterfall/falls)
    va-da-PAT

11) **река** (river)
    r'eh-KA

12) **древние руины** (ancient ruins)
    DR'EHV-n'i-jeh ru-I-ny

В пустыне бывает снег?
Does it ever snow in the desert?

Эта река самая длинная в стране.
This river is the longest in the country.

Я никогда не был в тропическом лесу.
I've never been in a tropical forest.

СПОРТ I (SPORTS I)

1) **стрельба из лука** (archery)
str'ehl'-BA iz LU-ka

2) **бокс** (boxing)
boks

3) **велосипедный спорт** (cycling)
v'eh-la-s'i-P'EHD-nyj sport

4) **фехтование** (fencing)
f'ehh-ta-VA-n'i-jeh

5) **футбол** (football/soccer)
fud-BOL

6) **регби** (rugby)
REHG-b'i

7) **настольный теннис/пинг-понг**
(table tennis/ping-pong)
nas-TOL'-nyj TEH-n'is/p'in-PONG

8) **волейбол** (volleyball)
va-l'ehj-BOL

9) **тяжёлая атлетика** (weightlift)
t'a-ZHO-la-ja at-L'EH-t'i-ka

10) **катание на коньках** (skating)
ka-TA-n'i-jeh na kan'-KAH

11) **паралимпийский спорт**
(paralympic sports)
pa-ra-l'im-P'IJ-sk'ij sport

12) **бейсбол** (baseball)
b'ehjz-BOL

13) **баскетбол** (basketball)
bas-k'ehd-BOL

Я фанат футбола.
I'm a football fan.

Мне нравится смотреть фехтование по телевизору.
I like watching fencing on TV.

Паралимпийский спорт заслуживает уважения.
Paralympic sports deserve respect.

СПОРТ II (SPORTS II)

1) **бадминтон** (badminton)
bad-m'in-TON

2) **гимнастика** (gymnastics)
g'im-NAS-t'i-ka

3) **гребля** (rowing)
GR'EH-bl'a

4) **скалолазание** (sport climbing)
ska-la-LA-za-n'i-jeh

5) **сёрфинг** (surfing)
s'or-f'ing

6) **теннис** (tennis)
TEH-n'is

7) **прыжки на батуте** (trampoline)
pryzh-K'I na ba-TU-t'eh

8) **борьба** (wrestling)
bar'-BA

9) **лыжный спорт** (skiing)
LYZH-nyj sport

10) **бобслей** (bobsled)
bap-SL'EHJ

11) **фигурное катание** (figure skating)
f'i-GUR-nə-jeh ka-TA-n'i-jeh

12) **плавание** (swimming)
PLA-va-n'i-jeh

13) **водное поло** (water polo)
VOD-nə-jeh PO-lə

14) **хоккей** (hockey)
ha-K'EHJ

Хоккей очень популярен в России.
Hockey is very popular in Russia.

Лыжный спорт не для меня.
Skiing is not for me.

Давай поиграем в бадминтон.
Let's go play badminton.

РОЖДЕСТВО (CHRISTMAS DAY)

1) **омела** (mistletoe)
a-MEH-la

2) **гирлянда** (garland)
g'ir-L'AN-da

3) **рождественская ёлка** (Christmas tree)
razh-D'EH-stv'ehn-ska-ja JOL-ka

4) **рождественские украшения** (Christmas decorations)
razh-D'EH-stv'ehn-sk'i-jeh uk-ra-SHEH-n'i-ja

5) **рождественские подарки** (Christmas gifts/presents)
razh-D'EH-stv'ehn-sk'i-jeh pa-DAR-k'i

6) **рождественский ужин** (Christmas dinner)
razh-D'EH-stv'ehn-sk'ij U-zhyn

7) **леденец** (lollipop/candy cane)
l'eh-d'eh-N'EHTS

8) **пряничный человечек** (gingerbread man)
PR'A-n'ich-nyj cheh-la-V'EH-chehk

9) **рождественский эльф** (Christmas elf)
razh-D'EH-stv'ehn-sk'ij ehl'f

10) **рождественская шапка** (Christmas hat)
razh-D'EH-stv'ehn-ska-ja SHAP-ka

11) **Дед Мороз** (Santa Claus)
d'et ma-ROS

12) **сани Деда Мороза** (Santa's sleigh)
SA-n'i D'EH-da ma-RO-za

13) **рождественская звезда** (Christmas star)
razh-D'EH-stv'ehn-ska-ja zv'ehz-DA

14) **снеговик** (snowman)
sn'eh-ga-V'IK

15) **свечи** (candles)
SV'EH-chi

Маленькие дети верят в Деда Мороза.
Little kids believe in Santa Claus.

Мы украсили дом гирляндами.
We decorated the house with garlands.

Давай слепим снеговика!
Let's make a snowman!

QUIZ #4

Use arrows to match the corresponding translations:

a. Christmas tree

b. judge

c. skating

d. boss

e. cliff

f. candles

g. teacher

h. truck

i. tennis

j. iron

k. animal trainer

l. shovel

m. swimming

n. desk

o. mountain

p. helicopter

1. свечи

2. рождественская ёлка

3. дрессировщик

4. вертолёт

5. теннис

6. судья

7. скала

8. гора

9. утюг

10. учитель

11. лопата

12. рабочий стол

13. грузовик

14. плавание

15. катание на коньках

16. начальник

Fill in the blank spaces with the options below (use each word only once):

Мне 17 лет. Пока, школа, пока _____! Мне нужно выбрать профессию. _____ оставил под ёлкой большой красивый блокнот. Я беру блокнот и _____ и записываю профессии. Мне нравится спорт, особенно _____, но я не хочу заниматься этим профессионально. Может быть, фотограф? Я буду путешествовать и фотографировать пейзажи: водопады, пустыни и _____. Или я стану _____! Хотя нет, это опасно. Я буду _____! Я буду сидеть в офисе, и у меня будет много работников. Но офис — это скучно: компьютер, принтер, _____. Нет, бизнес не для меня. А может быть, я буду пилотом? Но я боюсь _____! Я знаю! Я куплю _____ и полечу в путешествие. Но я обещал помочь маме. В саду меня ждёт _____, а потом ведро и _____. Пока, блокнот!

Дед Мороз

пожарным

воздушный шар

ручку

бизнесменом

швабра

борьба

школьная парта

самолётов

газонокосилка

вулканы

папки

МУЗЫКАЛЬНЫЕ ИНСТРУМЕНТЫ (MUSICAL INSTRUMENTS)

1) **акустическая гитара** (acoustic guitar)
a-kus-T'I-chehs-ka-ja g'i-TA-ra

2) **электрическая гитара** (electric guitar)
eh-l'ehk-TR'I-chehs-ka-ja g'i-TA-ra

3) **бас-гитара** (bass guitar)
bas-g'i-TA-ra

4) **барабаны** (drums)
ba-ra-BA-ny

5) **пианино** (piano)
p'i-a-N'I-nə

6) **труба** (trumpet)
tru-BA

7) **губная гармошка** (harmonica)
gub-NA-ja gar-MOSH-ka

8) **флейта** (flute)
FL'EHJ-ta

9) **кларнет** (clarinet)
klar-NEHT

10) **арфа** (harp)
AR-fa

11) **волынка** (bagpipes)
va-LYN-ka

12) **виолончель** (cello)
v'i-a-lan-CHEHL'

13) **скрипка** (violin)
SKR'IP-ka

14) **саксофон** (saxophone)
sak-sa-FON

Я хочу научиться играть на гитаре.
I want to learn how to play the guitar.

В школе он играл на барабанах.
He played the drums back at school.

Скрипка – это сложный инструмент.
Violin is a complex instrument.

ФРУКТЫ (FRUITS)

1) **клубника** (strawberry)
klub-N'I-ka

2) **папайя** (papaya)
pa-PA-ja

3) **слива** (plum)
SL'I-va

4) **дыня** (melon)
DY-n'a

5) **арбуз** (watermelon)
ar-BUS

6) **банан** (banana)
ba-NAN

7) **манго** (mango)
MAN-gə

8) **персик** (peach)
P'EHR-s'ik

9) **малина** (raspberry)
ma-L'I-na

10) **апельсин** (orange)
a-p'ehl'-S'IN

11) **лимон** (lemon)
l'i-MON

12) **ананас** (pineapple)
a-na-NAS

13) **лайм** (lime)
lajm

14) **виноград** (grapes)
v'i-na-GRAT

15) **вишня** (cherry)
V'ISH-n'a

16) **яблоко** (apple)
JAB-lə-kə

17) **груша** (pear)
GRU-sha

18) **грейпфрут** (grapefruit)
gr'ehjp-FRUT

19) **саусеп** (soursop)
sa-u-SEHP

20) **кокос** (coconut)
ka-KOS

У неё аллергия на клубнику.
She's allergic to strawberries.

Мне нужны вишни для торта.
I need cherries for the cake.

Бананы можно использовать в выпечке.
Bananas can be used in baking.

ОВОЩИ (VEGETABLES)

1) **цветная капуста** (cauliflower)
tsv'eht-NA-ja ka-PUS-ta

2) **спаржа** (asparagus)
SPAR-zha

3) **брокколи** (broccoli)
BRO-kə-l'i

4) **капуста** (cabbage)
ka-PUS-ta

5) **артишок** (artichoke)
art'i-SHOK

6) **брюссельская капуста** (Brussels sprout)
br'u-SEHL'-ska-ja ka-PUS-ta

7) **кукуруза** (corn)
ku-ku-RU-za

8) **салат** (lettuce)
sa-LAT

9) **шпинат** (spinach)
shp'i-NAT

10) **помидор** (tomato)
pa-m'i-DOR

11) **огурец** (cucumber)
a-gu-R'EHTS

12) **цукини** (zucchini)
tsu-K'I-n'i

13) **гриб** (mushroom)
gr'ip

14) **руккола** (arugula)
RU-kə-la

15) **баклажан** (eggplant)
bak-la-ZHAN

16) **болгарский перец** (bell pepper)
bal-GAR-sk'ij P'EH-r'ehts

17) **лук** (onion)
luk

18) **тыква** (pumpkin/squash)
TYK-va

19) **картофель** (potato)
kar-TO-f'ehl'

20) **листовая свёкла** (Swiss chard)
l'is-ta-VA-ja SV'OK-la

В спарже много железа.
Asparagus contains a lot of iron.

Я всегда плачу, когда режу лук.
I always cry when I cut onions.

Давай купим огурцы для салата.
Let's buy cucumbers for the salad.

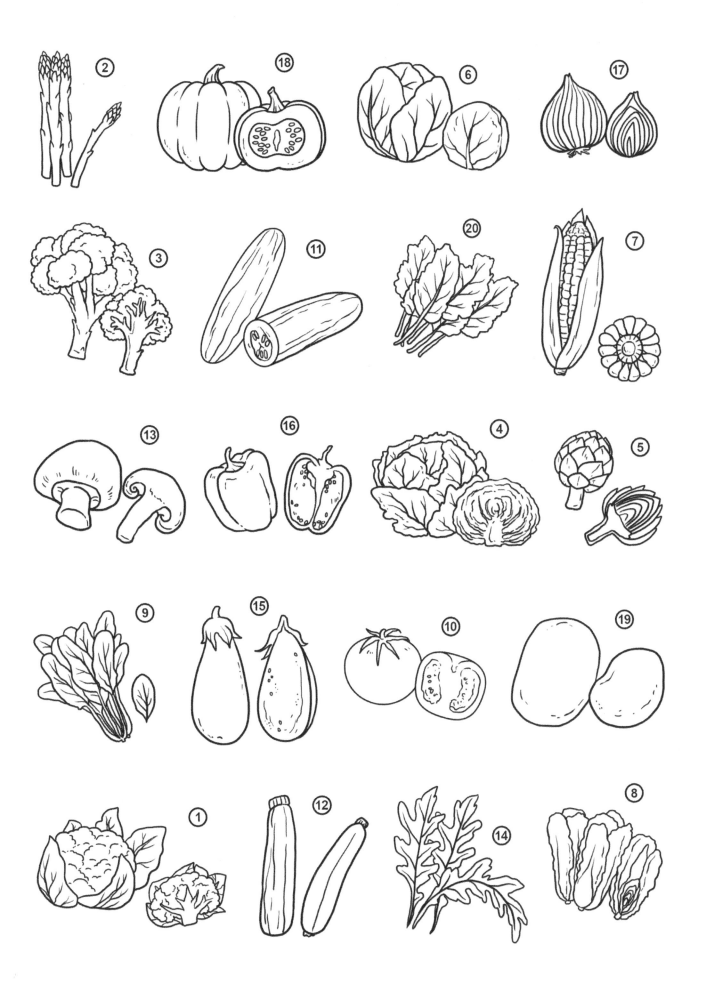

ТЕХНОЛОГИИ (TECHNOLOGY)

1) **мобильный** (mobile)
   ma-B'IL'-nyj

2) **устройство** (device)
   us-TROJ-stvə

3) **компьютер** (computer)
   kam-P'JU-tehr

4) **веб-камера** (web cam)
   vehb-KA-m'eh-ra

5) **флешка** (flash drive)
   FLEHSH-ka

6) **жёсткий диск** (hard drive)
   ZHOST-k'ij d'isk

7) **карта памяти** (memory card)
   KAR-ta PA-m'a-t'i

8) **картридер** (card reader)
   kart-R'I-dehr

9) **беспроводной** (wireless)
   bes-pra-vad-NOJ

10) **солнечная батарея** (solar panel)
    SOL-n'ehch-na-ja ba-ta-R'EH-ja

11) **принтер** (printer)
    PR'IN-tehr

12) **сканер** (scanner)
    SKA-nehr

Здесь есть беспроводной интернет?
Is there wireless internet here?

Мой мобильный разрядился.
My mobile died.

Ему нужна хорошая веб-камера для работы.
He needs a good web cam for his work.

НАУКА (SCIENCE)

1) **лаборатория** (laboratory)
   la-ba-ra-TO-r'i-ja

2) **исследователь** (researcher)
   is-SL'EH-də-və-t'ehl'

3) **вычисления** (calculations)
   vy-chis-L'EH-n'i-ja

4) **учёный** (scientist)
   u-CHO-nyj

5) **лабораторный халат** (lab coat)
   la-ba-ra-TOR-nyj ha-LAT

6) **эксперимент** (experiment)
   ehks-p'eh-r'i-M'EHNT

7) **защитные средства** (personal protective equipment)
   za-SCHIT-ny-jeh SR'EH-tstva

8) **тест** (test)
   tehst

9) **премия** (prize)
   PR'EH-m'i-ja

10) **риск** (risk)
    r'isk

11) **инструмент** (instrument)
    in-stru-M'EHNT

12) **статистика** (statistics)
    sta-T'IS-t'i-ka

Вы уверены, что эти вычисления правильные?
Are you sure that these calculations are correct?

Этот исследователь получил Нобелевскую премию.
This researcher has received the Nobel prize.

Нам не хватает защитных средств.
We're running short of personal protective equipment.

АСТРОНОМИЯ (ASTRONOMY)

1) **телескоп** (telescope)
t'eh-l'eh-SKOP

2) **солнце** (sun)
SON-tseh

3) **луна** (moon)
lu-NA

4) **галактика** (galaxy)
ga-LAK-t'i-ka

5) **пояс астероидов** (asteroid belt)
PO-jas as-teh-RO-i-dəf

6) **чёрная дыра** (black hole)
CHOR-na-ja dy-RA

7) **затмение** (eclipse)
zat-M'EH-n'i-jeh

8) **падающая звезда** (shooting star)
PA-da-ju-scha-ja zv'ehz-DA

9) **космическая станция** (space station)
kas-M'I-chehs-ka-ja STAN-tsy-ja

10) **белый карлик** (white dwarf)
B'EH-lyj KAR-l'ik

11) **красный гигант** (red giant)
KRAS-nyj g'i-GANT

12) **орбита** (orbit)
ar-B'I-ta

13) **созвездие** (constellation)
saz-V'EHZ-d'i-jeh

14) **тёмная энергия** (dark energy)
T'OM-nə-ja eh-NEHR-g'i-ja

15) **Плутон** (Pluto)
plu-TON

16) **Туманность** (Nebula)
tu-MAN-nəst'

17) **Меркурий** (Mercury)
m'her-KU-r'ij

18) **Венера** (Venus)
v'eh-N'EH-ra

19) **Земля** (Earth)
z'ehm-L'A

20) **Марс** (Mars)
mars

21) **Юпитер** (Jupiter)
ju-P'I-t'ehr

22) **Сатурн** (Saturn)
sah-TURN

23) **Уран** (Uranus)
u-RAN

24) **Нептун** (Neptune)
n'ehp-TUN

Я никогда не видел затмение.
I've never seen an eclipse.

Давай подарим ему телескоп на день рождения.
Let's give him a telescope for his birthday.

Смотри, падающая звезда! Давай, загадывай желание!
Look, it's a shooting star! Come on, make a wish!

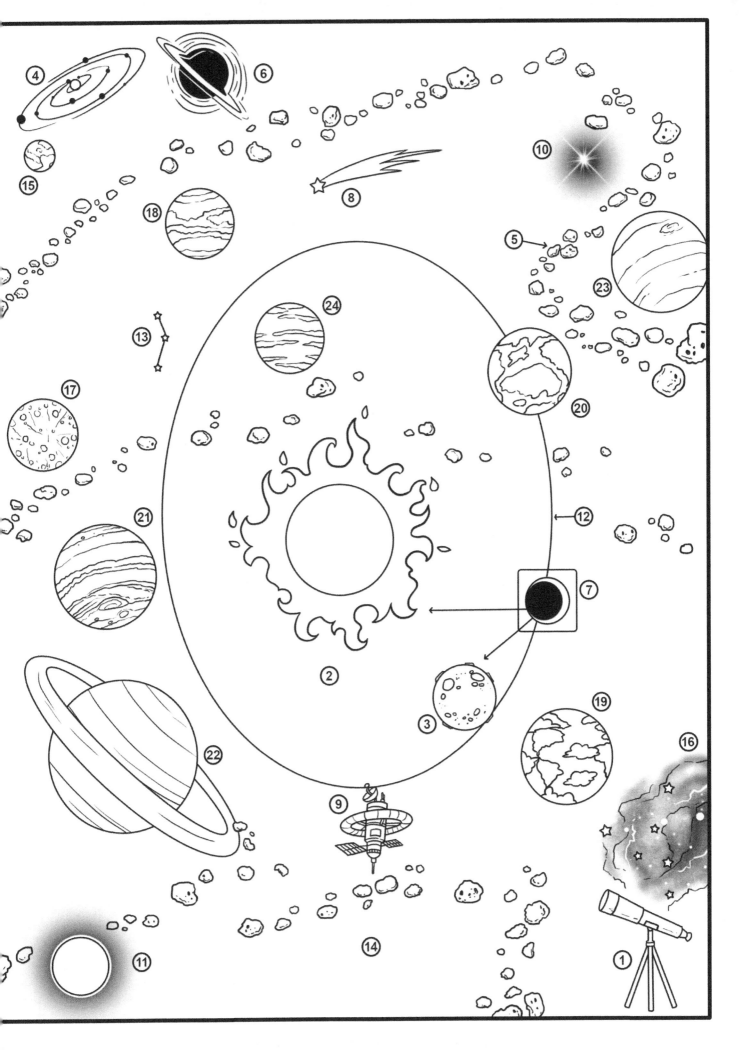

ГЕОГРАФИЯ (GEOGRAPHY)

1) **север** (north)
S'EH-v'ehr

2) **восток** (east)
vas-TOK

3) **юг** (south)
juk

4) **запад** (west)
ZA-pat

5) **экватор** (Equator)
eh-KVA-tər

6) **тропик Рака** (Tropic of Cancer)
TRO-p'ik RA-ka

7) **тропик Козерога** (Tropic of Capricorn)
TRO-p'ik ka-z'eh-RO-ga

8) **Южный полюс** (South Pole)
JUZH-nyj PO-l'us

9) **Северный полюс** (North Pole)
S'EH-v'ehr-nyj PO-l'us

10) **Полярный круг** (Arctic Circle)
pa-L'AR-nyj kruk

11) **континент** (continent)
kan-t'i-N'EHNT

12) **за морем** (overseas)
za MO-r'ehm

13) **Африка** (Africa)
A-fr'i-ka

14) **Азия** (Asia)
A-z'i-ja

15) **Северная Америка** (North America)
S'EH-v'ehr-na-ja a-M'EH-r'i-ka

16) **Центральная Америка** (Central America)
tsehn-TRAL'-na-ja a-M'EH-r'i-ka

17) **Южная Америка** (South America)
JUZH-na-ja a-M'EH-r'i-ka

18) **Европа** (Europe)
jehv-RO-pa

19) **Океания** (Oceania)
a-k'eh-A-n'i-ja

20) **Антарктика** (Antarctica)
an-TAR-kt'i-ka

21) **меридиан** (meridian)
m'eh-r'i-d'i-AN

22) **параллель** (parallel)
pa-ra-L'EHL'

23) **Атлантический океан** (Atlantic Ocean)
at-lan-T'I-chehs-k'i-j a-k'eh-AN

24) **Тихий океан** (Pacific Ocean)
T'I-h'ij a-k'eh-AN

Столица находится на юге страны.
The capital is in the South of the country.

Ты знаешь, как Тихий океан получил своё название?
Do you know how the Pacific Ocean got its name?

Я мечтаю увидеть Африку.
I dream of seeing Africa.

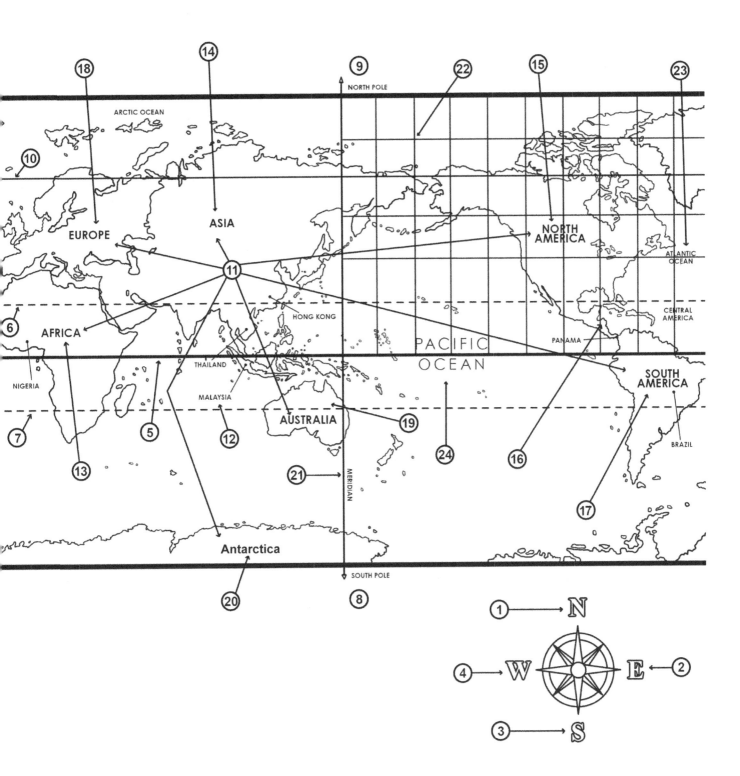

БОЛЬНИЦА (THE HOSPITAL)

1) **доктор** (doctor/medic)
DOK-tər

2) **медсестра** (nurse)
m'e-ts'ehs-TRA

3) **скорая помощь** (ambulance)
SKO-ra-ja PO-məsch

4) **аптечка первой помощи** (first aid kit)
ap-T'EHCH-ka P'EHR-vaj PO-mə-schi

5) **термометр** (thermometer)
t'ehr-MO-m'ehtr

6) **носилки** (stretcher)
na-S'IL-k'i

7) **шприц** (syringe)
shpr'its

8) **игла** (needle)
ig-LA

9) **стетоскоп** (stethoscope)
st'eh-ta-SKOP

10) **костыли** (crutches)
kas-ty-L'I

11) **инвалидное кресло** (wheelchair)
in-va-L'ID-nə-jeh KR'EHS-lə

12) **смотровая** (observation room)
sma-tra-VA-ja

13) **больничная койка** (hospital bed)
bal'-NICH-na-ja KOJ-ka

14) **инъекция** (injection)
in-JEHK-tsy-ja

15) **операция** (surgery)
a-p'eh-RA-tsy-ja

16) **история болезни** (medical history)
is-TO-r'i-ja ba-L'EHZ-n'i

17) **пациент** (patient)
pa-tsy-EHNT

18) **таблетки** (pill/tablet)
tab-L'EHT-k'i

Эти таблетки нужно принимать до еды.
These pills should be taken before meals.

Никогда не думал, что мне понадобятся костыли.
I never thought I would need crutches.

Операция длилась восемь часов.
The surgery lasted eight hours.

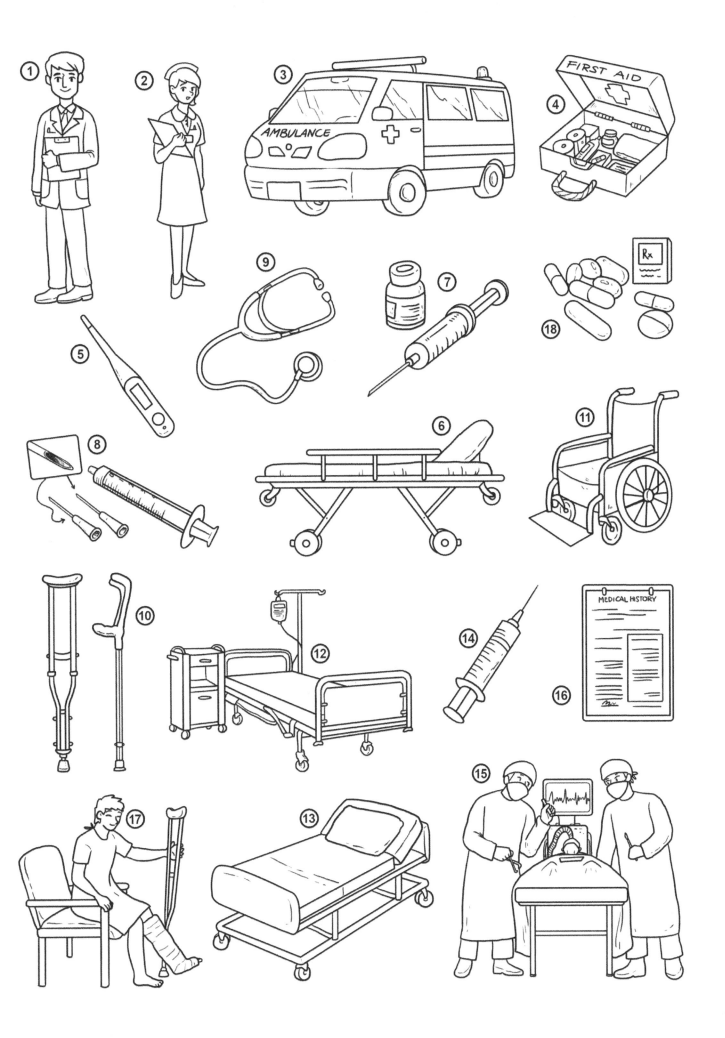

ФЕРМА (THE FARM)

1) **амбар** (barn)
am-BAR

2) **сарай/стойло** (cowshed/stable)
sa-RAJ/STOJ-lə

3) **фермер** (farmer)
F'EHR-m'ehr

4) **плуг** (plough)
pluh

5) **силосная башня** (silo)
S'I-ləs-nə-ja BASH-n'a

6) **мельница** (mill)
M'EHL'-n'i-tsa

7) **корыто для воды** (water trough)
ka-RY-tə dl'a va-DY

8) **курятник** (henhouse)
ku-R'AT-n'ik

9) **улей** (beehive)
U-l'ehj

10) **тюк сена** (hay bale)
t'uk S'EH-na

11) **скот** (cattle)
skot

12) **доить** (to milk)
da-IT'

13) **стадо** (herd/flock)
STA-də

14) **курица** (hen)
KU-r'i-tsa

15) **колодец** (well)
ka-LO-d'ehts

16) **система полива** (irrigation system)
s'is-T'EH-ma pa-L'I-va

17) **пугало** (scarecrow)
PU-gə-lə

18) **грунтовая дорога** (dirt road)
grun-TO-və-ja da-RO-ga

Птицы совсем не боятся нашего пугала.
Birds are not afraid of our scarecrow at all.

Вчера волк напал на стадо нашего соседа.
A wolf attacked our neighbor's herd yesterday.

Ты умеешь доить коров?
Can you milk cows?

QUIZ #5

Use arrows to match the corresponding translations:

a. potato

b. sun

c. melon

d. nurse

e. flash drive

f. trumpet

g. mill

h. device

i. Earth

j. syringe

k. harp

l. onion

m. West

n. cattle

o. apple

p. scientist

1. скот

2. дыня

3. труба

4. Земля

5. картофель

6. учёный

7. лук

8. медсестра

9. мельница

10. запад

11. солнце

12. флешка

13. устройство

14. яблоко

15. арфа

16. шприц

Fill in the blank spaces with the options below (use each word only once):

Я _____ и работаю в лаборатории. Мои друзья фермеры. Они живут на _____ страны. Они пригласили меня в гости, и я с радостью согласился! Никаких компьютеров, веб-камер и других _____. Только свежий воздух, природа, коровы и _____. А ещё мои друзья выращивают овощи: картофель, тыквы и _____. Я купил экзотические фрукты: папайю и _____. Мы встретились, пообедали, и мои друзья пошли доить коров. Я хотел помочь им, но корова ударила меня копытом прямо по голове! Я подумал, что это _____! В глазах стало темно. Мои друзья вызвали _____. Доктор сказал, что всё хорошо. Вечером мы сидели на крыльце и смотрели на _____. Мой друг играл на _____, и я забыл про случай с коровой.

востоке	скорую помощь
гитаре	курицы
затмение	учёный
помидоры	ананас
луну	устройств

ЕДА (FOOD)

1) **изюм** (raisins)
i-Z′UM

2) **грецкие орехи** (walnuts)
GR′EH-tsk′i-jeh a-R′EH-h′i

3) **мясо** (meat)
M′A-sə

4) **баранина** (lamb)
ba-RA-n′i-na

5) **рыба** (fish)
RY-ba

6) **курица** (chicken)
KU-r′i-tsa

7) **индейка** (turkey)
in-D′EHJ-ka

8) **мёд** (honey)
m′ot

9) **сахар** (sugar)
SA-har

10) **соль** (salt)
sol′

11) **перец** (pepper)
P′EH-r′ehts

12) **бекон** (bacon)
b′eh-KON

13) **сосиски** (sausages)
sa-S′IS-k′i

14) **кетчуп** (ketchup)
K′EHT-chup

15) **майонез** (mayonnaise)
ma-ja-NEHZ

16) **горчица** (mustard)
gar-CHI-tsa

17) **варенье** (jam)
va-R′EH-n′jeh

18) **сливочное масло** (butter)
SL′I-vəch-nə-jeh MAS-lə

19) **сок** (juice)
sok

20) **молоко** (milk)
ma-la-KO

Я вегетарианец, и не ем мясо.
I'm a vegetarian and don't eat meat.

В этом супе слишком много соли.
There is too much salt in this soup.

Пожалуйста, не забудь купить рыбу!
Please, don't forget to buy fish!

БЛЮДА (DISHES)

1) **лазанья** (lasagna)
   la-ZAN'-ja

2) **картофельная тортилья** (potato omelette)
   kar-TO-f'el'-na-ja tar-T'IL'-ja

3) **мясной рулет** (meatloaf)
   m'as-NOJ ru-L'EHT

4) **жареная лапша** (fried noodles)
   ZHA-r'eh-na-ja lap-SHA

5) **макароны с сыром** (macaroni and cheese)
   ma-ka-RO-ny s SY-rəm

6) **паэлья** (paella)
   pa-EHL'-ja

7) **рёбрышки барбекю** (barbecue ribs)
   R'OB-rysh-k'i bar-b'eh-K'U

8) **кукурузный хлеб** (cornbread)
   ku-ku-RUZ-nyj hl'ehp

9) **спринг-роллы** (spring rolls)
   spr'ing-ROL-ly

10) **чизбургер** (cheeseburger)
    CHIZ-bur-g'ehr

11) **жареная курица** (fried chicken)
    ZHA-r'eh-na-ja KU-r'i-tsa

12) **салат Цезарь** (Caesar salad)
    sah-LAT TSEH-zar'

13) **луковый суп** (onion soup)
    LU-kə-vyj sup

14) **капустный салат** (coleslaw)
    ka-PUS-nyj sa-LAT

15) **острые куриные крылышки** (spicy chicken wings)
    O-stry-jeh ku-R'I-ny-jeh KRY-lysh-k'i

16) **печенье с шоколадом** (chocolate-chip cookies)
    p'eh-CHEHN'-jeh s sha-ka-LA-dəm

17) **лаймовый пирог** (key lime pie)
    LAJ-mə-vyj p'i-ROH

18) **чизкейк** (cheesecake)
    chiz-K'EHJK

Давай закажем луковый суп и макароны с сыром.
Let's order some onion soup and macaroni with cheese.

Ты можешь дать мне твой рецепт лаймового пирога?
Can you share your key lime pie recipe with me?

Я на диете, но не могу устоять перед жареной курицей.
I'm on a diet but I can't resist fried chicken.

МОРЕПРОДУКТЫ (SEAFOOD)

1) **анчоусы** (anchovy)
an-CHO-u-sy

2) **треска** (cod)
tr'ehs-KA

3) **краб-паук** (spider crab)
krap-pa-UK

4) **скумбрия** (mackerel)
SKUM-br'i-ja

5) **лобстер** (lobster)
LOP-stehr

6) **эскалоп** (escalope)
ehs-ka-LOP

7) **люциан** (snapper)
l'u-tsi-AHN

8) **лососевая икра** (salmon roe)
la-SO-s'eh-va-ja ik-RA

9) **краб** (crab)
krap

10) **устрицы** (oysters)
US-tr'i-tsy

11) **угорь** (eel)
u-gor'

12) **креветки** (shrimp)
kr'eh-V'EH-tki

Тебе не кажется, что эти креветки слишком дорогие?
Don't you think that these shrimps are too expensive?

Скумбрия – очень жирная рыба.
Mackerel is a very fatty fish.

Давай сделаем бутерброды с лососевой икрой.
Let's make sandwiches with salmon roe.

ФИГУРЫ (SHAPES)

1) **круг** (circle)
   kruk

2) **овал** (oval)
   a-VAL

3) **треугольник** (triangle)
   tr'eh-u-GOL'-n'ik

4) **прямоугольник** (rectangle)
   pr'a-ma-u-GOL'-n'ik

5) **квадрат** (square)
   kvad-RAT

6) **трапеция** (trapezoid)
   tra-P'EH-tsy-ja

7) **ромб** (rhombus)
   romp

8) **куб** (cube)
   kup

9) **пятиугольник** (pentagon)
   p'a-t'i-u-GOL'-n'ik

10) **шестиугольник** (hexagon)
    shehs-t'i-u-GOL'-n'ik

11) **стрела** (arrow)
    str'eh-LA

12) **крест** (cross)
    kr'ehst

13) **сердце** (heart)
    S'EHR-tseh

14) **звезда** (star)
    zv'ehz-DA

15) **цилиндр** (cylinder)
    tsy-L'INDR

16) **конус** (cone)
    KO-nus

17) **пирамида** (pyramid)
    p'i-ra-M'I-da

18) **сфера** (sphere)
    SF'EH-ra

19) **призма** (prism)
    PR'IZ-ma

Сердце – это символ любви.
The heart is the symbol of love.

Мне нравится узор из ромбов на твоём свитере.
I like the rhombus pattern on your sweater.

Я купила сыну игрушечную пирамиду.
I bought my son a toy pyramid.

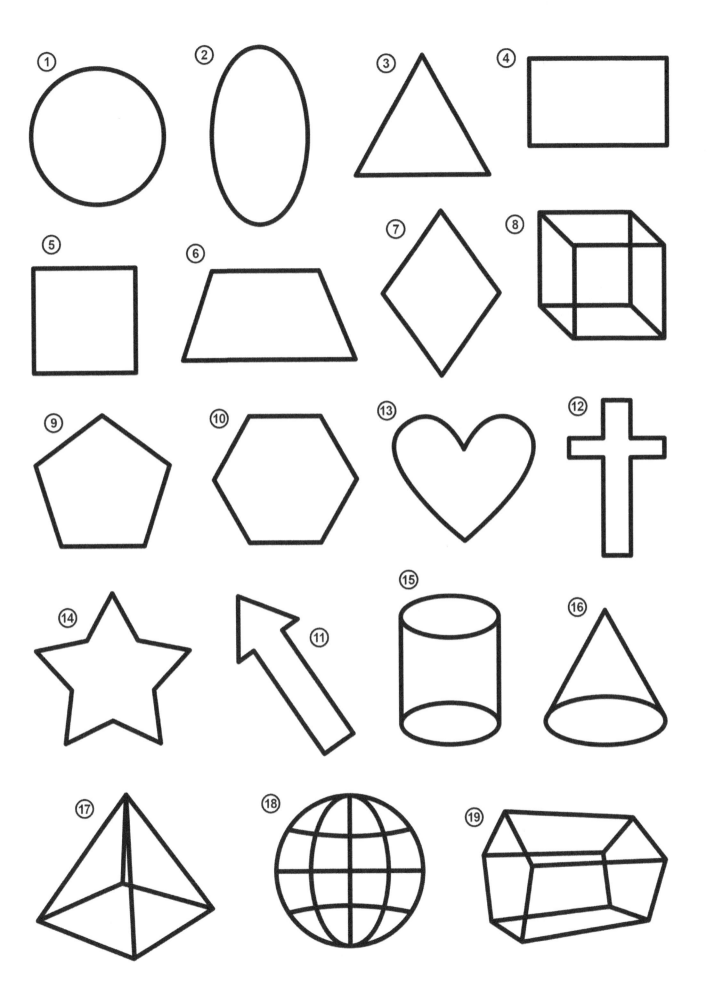

СУПЕРМАРКЕТ (THE SUPERMARKET)

1) **тележка** (shopping cart)
t'eh-L'EH-shka

2) **витрина** (cabinet/display case)
v'it-R'I-na

3) **покупатель** (customer)
pa-ku-PA-t'ehl'

4) **кассир** (cashier)
ka-S'IR

5) **чек** (receipt)
chehk

6) **пекарня** (bakery)
p'eh-KAR-n'a

7) **фрукты и овощи** (fruits and
vegetables)
FRUK-ty i O-va-schi

8) **мясо** (meat)
M'A-sə

9) **молочные продукты** (dairy
products)
ma-LOCH-ny-jeh pra-DUK-ty

10) **рыба** (fish)
RY-ba

11) **замороженные продукты** (frozen
food)
za-ma-RO-zheh-ny-jeh pra-DUK-ty

12) **курица** (poultry)
KU-r'i-tsa

13) **бобовые** (legumes)
ba-BO-vy-jeh

14) **закуски** (snacks)
za-KUS-k'i

15) **десерт** (dessert)
d'eh-S'EHRT

16) **напитки** (drinks)
na-P'IT-k'i

17) **бытовые товары** (household items)
by-ta-VY-jeh ta-VA-ry

18) **лента** (belt conveyor)
L'EHN-ta

Моя тележка полна продуктов и бытовых товаров.
My cart is full of groceries and household items.

Моя тётя работает кассиром в супермаркете.
My aunt works as a cashier at a supermarket.

Зимой я чаще покупаю замороженные овощи, а не свежие.
In winter I buy frozen vegetables more often than fresh ones.

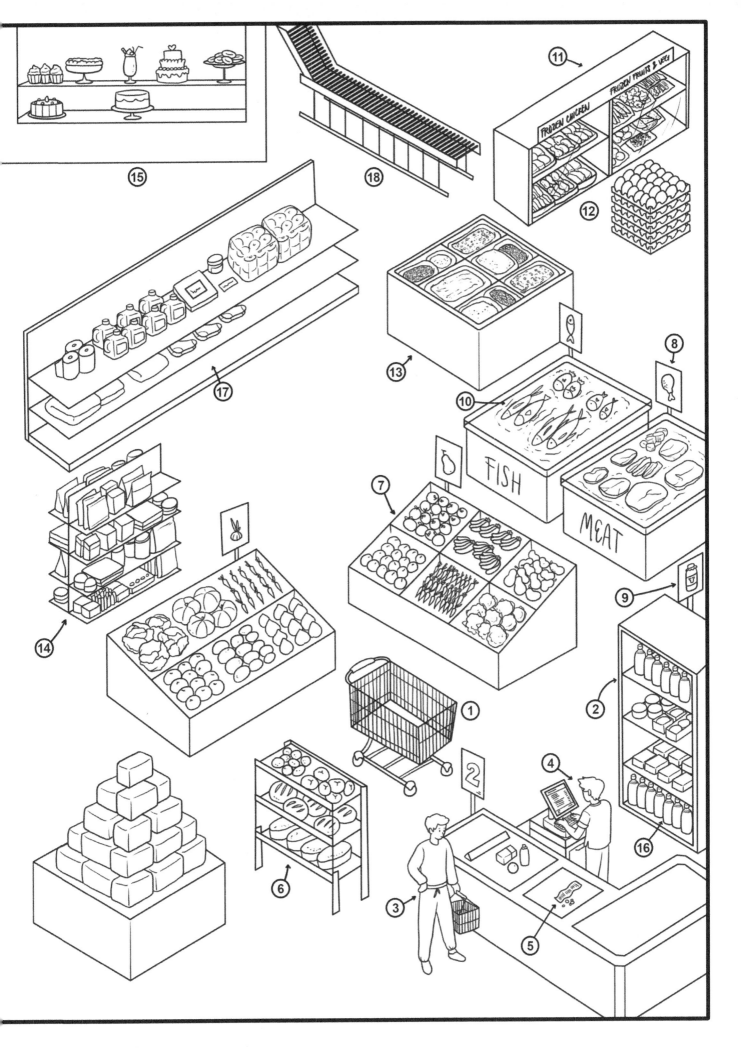

МЕДИА (MEDIA)

1) **журнал** (magazine)
zhur-NAL

2) **факс** (fax)
faks

3) **периодическое издание** (journal)
p'eh-r'i-a-D'I-chehs-kə-jeh iz-DA-n'i-jeh

4) **корреспонденция** (postal mail)
ka-r'ehs-pan-D'EH-tsy-ja

5) **письмо** (letter)
p'is'-MO

6) **радио** (radio)
RA-d'io

7) **комикс** (comic)
KO-m'iks

8) **книга** (book)
KN'I-ga

9) **фотография** (photography)
fa-ta-GRA-f'i-ja

10) **стационарный телефон** (landline phone)
sta-tsy-a-NAR-nyj t'eh-l'eh-FON

11) **телевизор** (TV)
t'eh-l'eh-V'I-zər

12) **фильмы** (movies)
F'IL'-my

13) **мобильный/сотовый телефон** (mobile/cell phone)
ma-B'IL'-nyj/SO-tə-vyj t'eh-l'eh-FON

14) **язык жестов** (sign language)
ja-ZYK ZHEHS-təf

Я выучил язык жестов, чтобы понимать своего немого друга.
I learned sign language to understand my mute friend.

Кто-нибудь ещё пользуется стационарным телефоном?
Does anyone still use the landline phone?

Мой сын тратит кучу денег на комиксы.
My son spends tons of money on comics.

ПАРК РАЗВЛЕЧЕНИЙ (THE FAIR/THE AMUSEMENT PARK)

1) **комната смеха** (house of mirrors)
   KOM-na-ta SM'EH-ha

2) **пиратский корабль** (pirate ship/boat swing)
   p'i-RA-tsk'ij ka-RABL'

3) **билетная касса** (ticket booth)
   b'i-L'EHT-na-ja KA-sa

4) **цепочная карусель** (swing ride)
   tseh-POCH-na-ja ka-ru-S'EHL'

5) **американские горки** (roller coaster)
   a-m'eh-r'i-KAN-sk'i-jeh GOR-k'i

6) **колесо обозрения** (Ferris wheel)
   ka-l'eh-SO a-baz-R'EH-n'i-ja

7) **карусель** (carousel/merry-go-round)
   ka-ru-S'EHL'

8) **автодром** (bumper cars)
   af-ta-DROM

9) **чашечки** (teacups/cup and saucer)
   CHA-sheh-chk'i

10) **маятник** (pendulum)
    MA-jat-n'ik

11) **игровые автоматы** (arcade room)
    ig-ra-VY-jeh af-ta-MA-ty

12) **корн-дог** (corn dog)
    korn-DOG

13) **мороженое** (ice cream)
    ma-RO-zheh-nə-jeh

14) **сахарная вата** (cotton candy)
    SA-har-na-ja VA-ta

15) **яблоко в карамели** (candy apple)
    JAB-lə-kə v ka-ra-M'EH-l'i

Я боюсь кататься на американских горках.
I'm afraid of riding a roller coaster.

Я пойду куплю билеты, а ты купи нам сахарную вату.
I'll go to buy tickets and you go and buy us a cotton candy.

Детям больше всего понравился маятник.
Kids liked the pendulum most of all.

ВАЖНЫЕ СОБЫТИЯ (LIFE EVENTS)

1) **рождение** (birth)
rahzh-D'EH-n'i-jeh

2) **крещение** (christening/baptism)
kr'eh-SCHEH-n'i-jeh

3) **первый день в школе** (first day of school)
P'HER-vyj d'ehn' v SHKO-l'eh

4) **подружиться** (make friends)
pa-dru-ZHY-ts'a

5) **день рождения** (birthday)
d'ehn' razh-D'EH-n'i-ja

6) **влюбиться** (fall in love)
vl'u-B'I-tsa

7) **окончание школы** (graduation)
a-kan-CHA-n'i-jeh SHKO-ly

8) **поступить в университет** (to start university/begin college)
pas-tu-P'IT' v u-n'i-v'her-s'i-T'EHT

9) **получить работу** (get a job)
pa-lu-CHIT' ra-BO-tu

10) **стать предпринимателем** (become an entrepreneur)
stat' pr'eht-pr'ih-n'i-MA-t'eh-l'ehm

11) **путешествовать по миру** (travel around the world)
pu-t'eh-SHEHS-tvə-vat' pa M'I-ru

12) **жениться/выйти замуж** (get married)
zheh-N'I-tsa/VYJ-t'i ZA-muzh

13) **родить ребёнка** (have a baby)
ra-D'IT' r'eh-B'ON-ka

14) **праздновать день рождения** (celebrate a birthday)
PRAZ-na-vat' d'ehn' razh-D'EH-n'i-ja

15) **выход на пенсию** (retirement)
VY-hət na P'EHN-s'i-ju

16) **смерть** (death)
sm'ehrt'

Рождение ребёнка — это самое волнующее событие в моей жизни.
Having a baby is the most exciting event in my life.

Мой племянник хочет стать предпринимателем.
My nephew wants to become an enterpreneur.

Они подружились в школе.
They became friends at school.

ПРИЛАГАТЕЛЬНЫЕ I (ADJECTIVES I)

1) **большой** (big)
bal'-SHOY

2) **маленький** (small)
MA-l'ehn'-k'ij

3) **громкий** (loud)
GROM-k'ij

4) **тихий** (silent)
T'I-h'ij

5) **длинный** (long)
DL'IN-nyj

6) **короткий** (short)
ka-ROT-k'ij

7) **широкий** (wide)
shy-RO-k'ij

8) **узкий** (narrow)
US-k'ij

9) **дорогой** (expensive)
da-ra-GOJ

10) **дешёвый** (cheap)
d'eh-SHO-vyj

11) **быстрый** (fast)
BYS-tryj

12) **медленный** (slow)
M'EH-dl'ehn-nyj

13) **пустой** (empty)
pus-TOJ

14) **полный** (full)
POL-nyj

15) **мягкий** (soft)
M'AH-k'ij

16) **твёрдый** (hard)
TV'OR-dyj

17) **высокий** (tall)
vy-SO-k'ij

18) **низкий** (short)
N'IS-k'ij

Этот стакан полный. Дай мне пустой, пожалуйста.
This glass is full. Give me an empty one, please.

Почему ты такой медленный?
Why are you so slow?

Мы купили большой дом.
We've bought a big house.

QUIZ #6

Use arrows to match the corresponding translations:

a. fried chicken

b. cod

c. shopping cart

d. honey

e. magazine

f. meat

g. arrow

h. death

i. shrimp

j. circle

k. jam

l. book

m. house of mirrors

n. coleslaw

o. fast

p. big

1. тележка

2. круг

3. капустный салат

4. большой

5. комната смеха

6. жареная курица

7. креветка

8. книга

9. журнал

10. смерть

11. варенье

12. треска

13. быстрый

14. мясо

15. мёд

16. стрела

Fill in the blank spaces with the options below (use each word only once):

Сегодня праздник – мой _____. Я не хотел большого праздника, просто _____ вечер дома. Я заказал устрицы и _____ и хотел просто сидеть дома и смотреть _____. Но утром пришли мои родители. Папа подарил мне _____, а мама испекла шикарный _____ – торт в форме _____ с изюмом и _____. А ещё она приготовила мой любимый _____.

Потом пришли мои друзья, и мы пошли в парк развлечений. Мы катались на _____, ели _____, а потом развлекались на _____. Это был чудесный день рождения! Лучше, чем сидеть дома и смотреть фильм!

тихий	сердца
сотовый телефон	лобстера
день рождения	колесе обозрения
сахарную вату	игровых автоматах
мясной рулет	фильм
десерт	грецкими орехами

ПРИЛАГАТЕЛЬНЫЕ II (ADJECTIVES II)

1) **новый** (new)
NO-vyj

2) **старый** (old)
STA-ryj

3) **удобный** (comfortable)
u-DOB-nyj

4) **неудобный** (uncomfortable)
n'eh-u-DOB-nyj

5) **опасный** (dangerous)
a-PAS-nyj

6) **раздражающий** (annoying)
raz-dra-ZHA-ju-schij

7) **вибрирующий** (shaky)
v'ib-R'I-ru-ju-schij

8) **полный** (complete)
POL-nyj

9) **неполный** (incomplete)
n'e-POL-nyj

10) **сломанный** (broken)
SLO-mə-nyj

11) **великолепный** (gorgeous)
v'eh-l'i-ka-L'EHP-nyj

12) **виртуозный** (virtuous)
v'ir-tu-OZ-nyj

13) **похожий** (similar)
pa-HO-zhyj

14) **разный** (different)
RAZ-nyj

15) **открытый** (open)
at-KRY-tyj

16) **закрытый** (closed)
zak-RY-tyj

Моя коллекция неполная без этой марки.
My collection is incomplete without this stamp.

Эти старые туфли более удобные, чем новые.
These old shoes are more comfortable than the new ones.

Зачем тебе эта сломанная игрушка?
Why do you need this broken toy?

НАРЕЧИЯ (ADVERBS)

1) **здесь** (here)
zd'ehs'

2) **там** (there)
tam

3) **возле** (near)
VOZ-l'eh

4) **далеко** (far)
da-l'eh-KO

5) **вверху** (up)
v-v'ehr-HU

6) **внизу** (down)
vn'i-ZU

7) **внутри** (inside)
vnut-R'I

8) **снаружи** (outside)
sna-RU-zhy

9) **впереди** (ahead)
vp'eh-r'eh-D'I

10) **за** (behind)
za

11) **нет** (no)
n'et

12) **да** (yes)
da

13) **сейчас** (now)
s'eh-CHAS

14) **хорошо** (well/good/right)
ha-ra-SHO

15) **плохо** (bad/wrong)
PLO-hə

Кто это за тобой?
Who is it behind you?

Я живу возле рынка.
I live near the market.

Что вы делаете сейчас?
What are you doing now?

НАПРАВЛЕНИЯ (DIRECTIONS)

1) **многоквартирный дом** (apartment building)
MNO-ga-kvar-T'IR-nyj dom

2) **площадь** (square)
PLO-schat'

3) **парк** (park)
park

4) **метро** (subway)
m'eht-RO

5) **угол** (corner)
U-gəl

6) **авеню** (avenue)
a-v'eh-N'U

7) **улица** (street)
U-l'i-tsa

8) **автобусная остановка** (bus stop)
af-TO-bus-na-ja as-ta-NOF-ka

9) **светофор** (traffic lights)
sv'eh-ta-FOR

10) **переход** (crossing/crosswalk)
p'eh-r'eh-HOT

11) **вверх** (up)
vv'ehrh

12) **вниз** (down)
vn'is

13) **налево** (left)
na-L'E-və

14) **направо** (right)
na-PRA-və

15) **дорожные знаки** (road signs)
da-ROZH-ny-jeh ZNA-k'i

16) **ГАИ** (traffic police)
ga-I

Идите по этой улице и поверните направо.
Go down the street and turn right.

Светофор на углу сломался.
The traffic lights on the corner are broken.

Что значит этот дорожный знак?
What does this road sign mean?

РЕСТОРАН (THE RESTAURANT)

1) **менеджер** (manager)
MEH-neh-dzhehr

2) **стол** (table)
stol

3) **меню** (menu)
m'eh-N'U

4) **блюдо** (dish)
BL'U-də

5) **аперитив** (appetizer)
a-p'eh-r'ih-T'IF

6) **закуска** (starter)
za-KUS-ka

7) **главное блюдо** (main course)
GLAV-nə-jeh BL'U-də

8) **десерт** (dessert)
d'eh-S'EHRT

9) **ужин** (dinner)
U-zhyn

10) **повар** (cook)
PO-var

11) **официант** (waiter)
a-f'i-tsy-ANT

12) **официантка** (waitress)
a-f'i-tsy-ANT-ka

13) **чаевые** (tip)
cha-jeh-VY-jeh

14) **высокий стул** (high chair)
vy-SO-k'ij stul

15) **винная карта** (wine list)
V'IN-na-ja KAR-ta

16) **кондитер** (pastry chef)
kan-D'I-t'ehr

Сколько оставим на чаевые?
How much shall we leave as a tip?

Моя бабушка работает кондитером в кафе.
My grandmother works as a pastry chef in a cafe.

Официант, принесите нам меню, пожалуйста.
Waiter, bring us the menu, please.

ТОРГОВЫЙ ЦЕНТР (THE MALL)

1) **этаж** (floor)
eh-TAZH

2) **аквариум** (aquarium)
ak-VA-r'i-um

3) **фуд-корт** (food court)
fut-KORT

4) **лифт** (elevator)
l'ift

5) **эскалатор** (escalators)
ehs-ka-LA-tər

6) **аварийный выход** (emergency exit)
a-va-R'IJ-nyj VY-hət

7) **салон красоты** (beauty salon)
sa-LON kra-sa-TY

8) **магазин одежды** (clothing store)
ma-ga-Z'IN a-D'EHZH-dy

9) **игровая комната** (playground)
ig-ra-VA-ja KOM-na-ta

10) **охранник** (security guard)
ah-RAN-n'ik

11) **камера наблюдения** (surveillance camera)
KA-m'eh-ra nab-l'u-D'EH-n'i-ja

12) **пекарня** (bakery)
p'eh-KAR-n'a

13) **магазин спорттоваров** (sports store)
ma-ga-Z'IN sport-ta-VA-rəf

14) **фонтан** (fountain)
fan-TAN

Я работаю охранником в торговом центре.
I work as a security guard in a mall.

Давай оставим детей в игровой комнате.
Let's leave the kids at the playground.

Мои родственники открыли магазин одежды.
My relatives opened a clothing store.

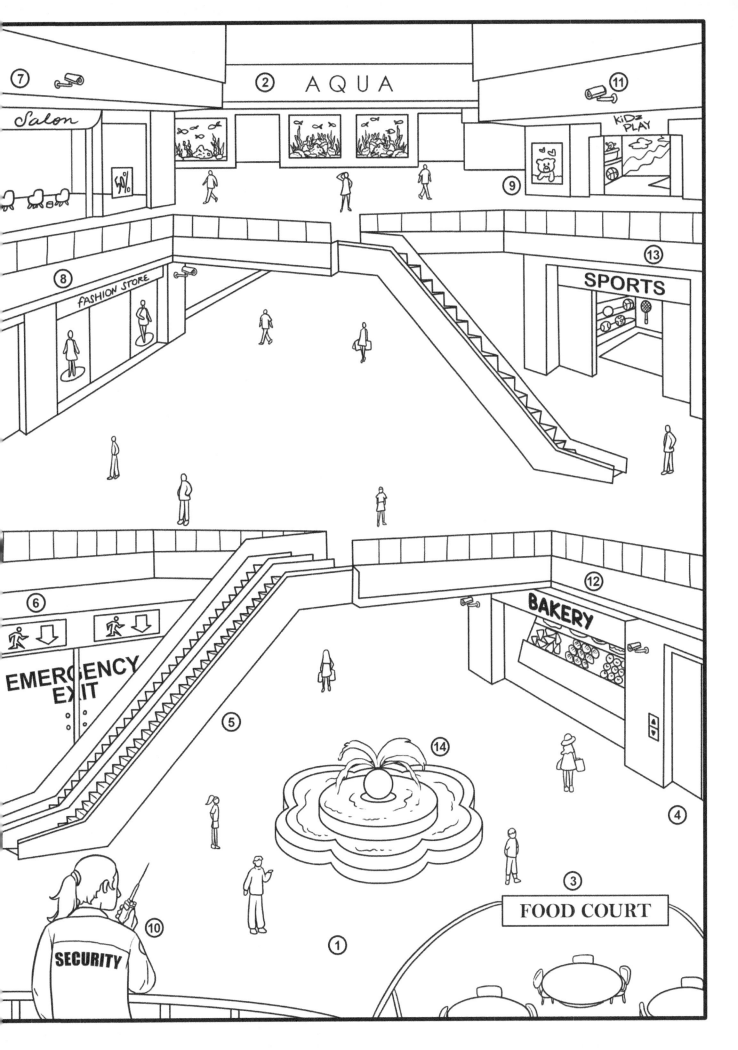

ГЛАГОЛЫ I (VERBS I)

1) **разговаривать** (to talk)
raz-ga-VA-r'i-vat'

2) **пить** (to drink)
p'it'

3) **кушать** (to eat)
KU-shat'

4) **гулять** (to walk)
gu-L'AT'

5) **открыть** (to open)
at-KRYT'

6) **закрыть** (to close)
za-KRYT'

7) **дать** (to give)
dat'

8) **видеть** (to see)
v'i-D'EHT'

9) **идти за** (to follow)
i-T'I za

10) **обнимать** (to hug)
ab-n'i-MAT'

11) **целовать** (to kiss)
tseh-lə-VAT'

12) **покупать** (to buy)
pa-KU-pat'

13) **слушать** (to listen)
SLU-shat'

14) **петь** (to sing)
p'eht'

15) **танцевать** (to dance)
tan-tseh-VAT'

Мы покупаем овощи на рынке.
We buy vegetables at the market.

Почему ты идёшь за мной?
Why are you following me?

Я совсем не умею петь.
I can't sing at all.

ГЛАГОЛЫ II (VERBS II)

1) **писать** (to write)
p'i-SAT'

2) **читать** (to read)
chi-TAT'

3) **чистить** (to clean)
CHIS-t'it'

4) **поднимать** (to pick up)
pad-n'i-MAT'

5) **найти** (to find)
naj-T'I

6) **мыть** (to wash)
myt'

7) **смотреть** (to watch)
smat-R'EHT'

8) **чинить** (to fix)
chi-N'IT'

9) **думать** (to think)
DU-mat'

10) **брать** (to take)
brat'

11) **резать** (to cut)
R'EH-zat'

12) **останавливаться** (to stop)
as-ta-NAV-l'i-va-tsa

13) **плакать** (to cry)
PLA-kat'

14) **улыбаться** (to smile)
u-ly-BA-tsa

15) **помогать** (to help)
pa-ma-GAT'

Я люблю читать в постели.
I like reading in bed.

Нужно мыть руки перед едой.
One should wash hands before meals.

Пожалуйста, перестань плакать!
Please, stop crying!

СТРОИТЕЛЬСТВО I (CONSTRUCTION I)

1) **кран** (crane)
   kran

2) **сигнальная лента** (hazard tape)
   s'ig-NAL'-na-ja L'EHN-ta

3) **дорожный конус** (traffic cone)
   da-ROZH-nyj KO-nus

4) **строительная лопата** (construction shovel)
   stra-I-t'ehl'-nə-j'a la-PA-ta

5) **молоток** (hammer)
   ma-la-TOK

6) **кусачки** (wire cutters)
   ku-SACH-k'i

7) **валик** (paint roller)
   VA-l'ik

8) **бензопила** (chainsaw)
   b'ehn-za-p'i-LA

9) **дрель** (drill)
   dr'ehl'

10) **отбойный молоток** (jackhammer)
    at-BOJ-nyj ma-la-TOK

11) **плоскогубцы** (pliers)
    plas-ka-GUP-tsy

12) **отвёртка** (screwdriver)
    at-V'OR-tka

Передай мне отвёртку, пожалуйста.
Give me the screwdriver, please.

Мы красили стены валиком.
We were painting the walls with a paint roller.

Этот молоток слишком тяжёлый для меня.
This hammer is too heavy for me.

СТРОИТЕЛЬСТВО II (CONSTRUCTION II)

1) **ящик с инструментами** (toolbox)
   JA-schik s in-stru-M'EH-ta-m'i

2) **каска** (work helmet/hard hat)
   KAS-ka

3) **чертёж** (blueprint)
   chehr-T'OZH

4) **трубы** (pipes)
   TRU-by

5) **мастерок** (trowel)
   mas-t'eh-ROK

6) **бетономешалка** (concrete mixer)
   b'eh-TO-nə-m'eh-SHAL-ka

7) **кирпич** (brick)
   k'ir-P'ICH

8) **строительные материалы** (building materials)
   stra-I-t'ehl'-ny-jeh ma-t'eh-r'i-A-ly

9) **плитка** (tiles)
   PL'IT-ka

10) **цемент** (cement)
    tseh-M'EHNT

11) **песок** (sand)
    p'eh-SOK

12) **гравий** (gravel)
    GRA-v'ij

Эти кирпичи недорогие.
These bricks are inexpensive.

Мы купили дедушке ящик с инструментами.
We've bought a toolbox for our grandfather.

У нас недостаточно гравия для бетона.
We don't have enough gravel for the concrete.

QUIZ #7

Use arrows to match the corresponding translations:

a. floor

b. near

c. subway

d. buy

e. open

f. wash

g. traffic police

h. starter

i. beauty salon

j. virtuous

k. outside

l. dinner

m. blueprint

n. follow

o. screwdriver

p. brick

1. чертёж

2. этаж

3. покупать

4. отвёртка

5. салон красоты

6. ГАИ

7. возле

8. виртуозный

9. мыть

10. ужин

11. идти за

12. метро

13. открытый

14. закуска

15. снаружи

16. кирпич

Fill in the blank spaces with the options below (use each word only once):

Мой день начался _____. Я работаю _____ в ресторане. Моя работа начинается рано, а живу я далеко. Поэтому утром я иду на _____. У меня было _____ настроение. На голове у меня были наушники, я шла, _____ музыку и _____. Поэтому я не заметила _____ плитку на тротуаре! Я наступила на неё и упала. Мне было очень больно, и я даже хотела _____. Я успокоилась, но мой день испорчен!

автобусную остановку   сломанную

пела   плохо

поваром   плакать

хорошее   слушала

РАСТЕНИЯ И ДЕРЕВЬЯ (PLANTS AND TREES)

1) **полевой цветок** (wildflower)
   pa-l'eh-VOJ tsv'eh-TOK

2) **лекарственное растение** (herb)
   l'eh-KAR-stv'ehn-na-jeh ras-T'EH-n'i-jeh

3) **гриб** (mushroom)
   gr'ip

4) **сорняк** (weed)
   sar-N'AK

5) **водоросли** (seaweed)
   VO-də-rəsl'i

6) **папоротник** (fern)
   PA-pa-rat-n'ik

7) **камыш** (reed)
   ka-MYSH

8) **бамбук** (bamboo)
   bam-BUK

9) **плющ** (ivy)
   pl'usch

10) **мох** (moss)
    moh

11) **трава** (grass)
    tra-VA

12) **пальма** (palm tree)
    PAL'-ma

13) **мангры** (mangrove)
    MAN-gry

14) **кактус** (cactus)
    KAK-tus

Эти сорняки в саду сводят меня с ума!
These weeds in the garden drive me mad!

Эта мебель сделана из бамбука.
This furniture is made of bamboo.

Летом мы собираем лекарственные растения.
We collect herbs in summer.

КАРНАВАЛ (THE CARNIVAL)

1) **маска** (mask)
   MAS-ka

2) **костюм** (costume/outfit)
   kas-T'UM

3) **платформа** (float)
   plat-FOR-ma

4) **цветы** (flowers)
   tsv'eh-TY

5) **малый барабан** (snare drum)
   MA-lyj ba-ra-BAN

6) **клоун** (clown)
   KLO-un

7) **супергерой** (superhero)
   su-p'ehr-g'eh-ROJ

8) **принцесса** (princess)
   pr'in-TSEH-sa

9) **космонавт** (astronaut)
   kas-ma-NAFT

10) **мим** (mime)
    m'im

11) **заключённый** (prisoner)
    zak-l'u-CHON-nyj

12) **бытовой прибор** (household appliance)
    by-ta-VOJ pr'i-BOR

13) **фея** (fairy)
    F'EH-ja

14) **дровосек** (lumberjack)
    dra-va-S'EHK

Моя дочь нарядилась феей.
My daughter dressed up as a fairy.

Не все клоуны смешные.
Not all clowns are funny.

Заключённый сбежал ночью.
The prisoner escaped at night.

МАСТЕРСКАЯ (THE WORKSHOP)

1) **инструмент** (tool)
in-stru-M'EHNT

2) **шорное ремесло** (saddlery)
SHOR-nə-jeh r'eh-m'ehs-LO

3) **столярничество**
(carpentry/woodwork)
sta-L'AR-n'i-cheh-stvə

4) **драпировка** (upholstery/tapestry)
dra-p'i-ROF-ka

5) **сапожное ремесло**
(shoemaking/shoerepair)
sa-POZH-nə-jeh r'eh-m'ehs-LO

6) **ювелир** (jeweler)
ju-v'eh-L'IR

7) **кузнец** (blacksmith)
kuz-N'EHTS

8) **механик** (mechanic)
m'eh-HA-n'ik

9) **текстиль** (textile)
t'ehk-ST'IL'

10) **пекарня** (bakery)
p'eh-KAR-n'a

11) **бижутерия** (costume jewelry)
b'i-zhu-TEH-r'i-ja

12) **обувь** (footwear)
O-buf'

13) **обслуживание** (maintenance)
ap-SLU-zhy-va-n'i-jeh

14) **ремонт** (repair)
r'eh-MONT

15) **живопись** (painting)
ZHY-və-p'is'

16) **выпечка** (pastry)
VY-p'ehch-ka

Он унаследовал пекарню от отца.
He inherited the bakery from his father.

Эта бижутерия ручной работы.
This costume jewelry is handmade.

Я занимаюсь живописью с пяти лет.
I've been into painting since I was five.

МАГАЗИН ПРОДУКТОВ (THE GROCERY STORE)

1) **паста** (pasta)
   PAS-ta

2) **рис** (rice)
   r'is

3) **овсянка** (oat)
   af-S'AN-ka

4) **хлеб** (bread)
   hl'ehp

5) **масла** (oils)
   mas-LA

6) **соусы** (sauces)
   SO-u-sy

7) **заправки к салату** (salad dressings)
   zap-RAF-k'i k sa-LA-tu

8) **приправы** (condiments)
   pr'ip-RA-vy

9) **консервы** (canned goods)
   kan-S'EHR-vy

10) **ветчина** (ham)
    v'eht-chi-NA

11) **сыр** (cheese)
    syr

12) **арахисовое масло** (peanut butter)
    a-RA-h'i-sə-və-jeh MAS-lə

13) **конфета** (candy)
    kan-F'EH-ta

14) **бобы** (beans)
    ba-BY

15) **кофе** (coffee)
    KO-f'eh

16) **чай** (tea)
    chaj

Как можно есть овсянку каждое утро?
How can one eat oats every morning?

Эти приправы слишком острые.
These condiments are too spicy.

Эти конфеты шоколадные?
Are these candies chocolate ones?

ПУТЕШЕСТВИЕ I (TRAVEL AND LIVING I)

1) **хозяин** (host)
   ha-Z'A-in

2) **турист** (tourist)
   tu-R'IST

3) **путешественник** (traveler)
   pu-t'eh-SHEH-stv'ehn-n'ik

4) **багаж** (luggage)
   ba-GAZH

5) **ручная кладь** (hand luggage)
   ruch-NA-ja klad'

6) **фотоаппарат** (camera)
   FO-ta-ap-pa-RAT

7) **отель** (hotel)
   a-TEHL'

8) **хостел** (hostel)
   HOS-tehl

9) **гостиница** (hotel/inn)
   gas-T'I-n'i-tsa

10) **домик** (cabin)
    DO-m'ik

11) **палатка** (tent)
    pa-LAT-ka

12) **полёт** (flight)
    pa-L'OT

13) **отправление** (departure)
    at-prav-L'EH-n'i-jeh

14) **прибытие** (arrival)
    pr'i-BY-t'i-jeh

Я не помню время твоего прибытия.
I don't remember your arrival time.

Она взяла интервью у знаменитого путешественника.
She interviewed a famous traveler.

У нас есть домик в лесу.
We've got a cabin in the woods.

ПУТЕШЕСТВИЕ II (TRAVEL AND LIVING II)

1) **город** (town)
GO-rət

2) **карта** (map)
KAR-ta

3) **автобусная остановка** (bus stop)
af-TO-bus-na-ja as-ta-NOF-ka

4) **такси** (taxi)
tak-S'I

5) **аренда автомобилей** (car rental)
a-R'EHN-da af-ta-ma-B'I-l'ehj

6) **железнодорожная станция** (train station)
zheh-L'EHZ-nə-da-ROZH-nə-ja STAN-tsy-ja

7) **аэропорт** (airport)
a-eh-ra-PORT

8) **паспорт** (passport)
PAS-pərt

9) **удостоверение личности** (ID/identification card)
u-das-tə-v'eh-R'EH-n'i-jeh L'ICH-nəs-t'i

10) **валюта** (currency)
va-L'U-ta

11) **наличные** (cash)
na-L'ICH-ny-jeh

12) **платёжная карточка** (debit card)
pla-T'OZH-na-j'a KAR-tə-chka

13) **кредитная карточка** (credit card)
kr'e-D'IT-nə-ja KAR-tə-chka

14) **туристический гид** (tourist guide)
tu-r'is-T'I-chehs-k'ij g'id

Какая валюта в этой стране?
What currency do they have in this country?

У вас есть карта города?
Do you have the city map?

Я буду платить наличными.
I'm paying in cash.

ИГРУШКИ (TOYS)

1) **мяч** (ball)
m'ach

2) **плюшевый медвежонок** (teddy bear)
PL'U-she-vyj m'ehd-v'eh-ZHO-nək

3) **поезд** (train)
PO-jehst

4) **скейтборд** (skateboard)
sk'ehjt-BORT

5) **кукла** (doll)
KUK-la

6) **гоночная машинка** (race car)
GO-nəch-na-ja ma-SHYN-ka

7) **робот** (robot)
RO-bət

8) **воздушный змей** (kite)
vaz-DUSH-nyj zm'ehj

9) **барабан** (drum)
ba-ra-BAN

10) **хула-хуп** (hula hoop)
hu-la-HUP

11) **тележка** (wagon)
t'eh-L'EHZH-ka

12) **фигурки** (blocks)
f'i-GUR-k'i

13) **ксилофон** (xylophone)
ks'i-la-FON

14) **грузовик** (truck)
gru-za-V'IK

15) **самолёт** (airplane)
sa-ma-L'OT

16) **кубики** (bricks)
KU-b'i-k'i

Сколько у тебя кукол?
How many dolls do you have?

Мне подарили робота на день рождения.
I was given a robot for my birthday.

Давай запустим воздушного змея!
Let's fly a kite!

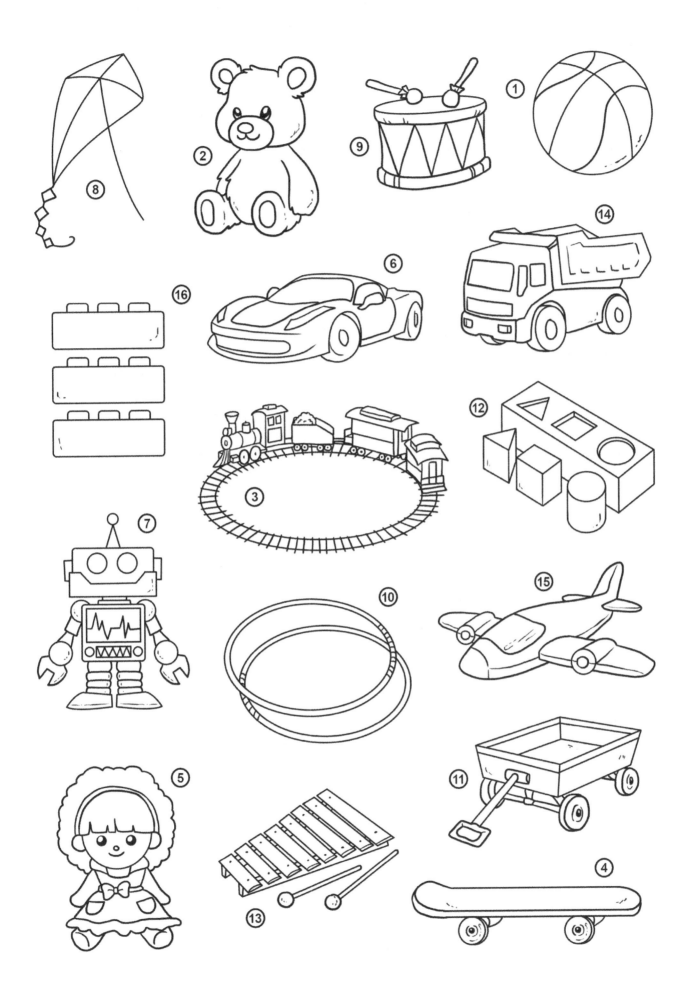

ДЕНЬ РОЖДЕНИЯ (THE BIRTHDAY PARTY)

1) **плакат на день рождения**
(birthday banner)
pla-KAT na d'en' razh-D'EH-n'i-ja

2) **украшения** (decorations)
uk-ra-SHEH-n'i-ja

3) **подарок** (present/gift)
pa-DA-rək

4) **столовые приборы** (tableware)
sta-LO-vy-jeh pr'i-BO-ry

5) **именинник/именинница** (birthday
person m./f.)
i-m'eh-N'IN-n'ik/i-m'eh-N'IN-n'i-tsa

6) **воздушный шар** (balloon)
vaz-DUSH-nyj shar

7) **праздничный торт** (birthday cake)
PRAZ-n'ich-nyj tort

8) **тарелки** (plates)
ta-R'EHL-k'i

9) **вилки** (forks)
V'IL-k'i

10) **ложки** (spoons)
LOSH-k'i

11) **чашки** (cups)
CHASH-k'i

12) **соломинка** (straw)
sa-LO-m'in-ka

13) **пиньята** (piñata)
p'ihn'-JA-ta

14) **свеча** (candle)
sv'eh-CHA

15) **колпак** (hat)
kal-PAK

16) **гости** (guests)
GOS-t'i

Кто здесь у нас именинник?
Who is the birthday person here?

Я купила бумажные тарелки для праздника.
I've bought carton plates for the party.

Посмотри, сколько здесь воздушных шаров!
Look how many balloons are here!

АНТОНИМЫ (OPPOSITES)

1) **чистый** (clean)
CHIS-tyj

2) **грязный** (dirty)
GR'AZ-nyj

3) **мало** (few)
MA-lə

4) **много** (many)
MNO-gə

5) **атаковать** (attack)
a-ta-ka-VAT'

6) **защищаться** (defense)
za-schi-SCHA-tsa

7) **прямой** (straight)
pr'a-MOJ

8) **изогнутый** (curved)
i-ZOG-nu-tyj

9) **вместе** (together)
VM'EHS-t'eh

10) **в разлуке** (separated)
v raz-LU-k'eh

11) **молодой** (young)
ma-la-DOJ

12) **старый** (old)
STA-ryj

13) **богатство** (wealth)
ba-GA-tstvə

14) **бедность** (poverty)
B'E-dnast'

15) **вогнутый** (concave)
VO-gnu-tyj

16) **выпуклый** (convex)
VY-puk-lyj

Мы никогда не будем вместе.
We will never be together.

У тебя много друзей?
Do you have many friends?

Я уже не молодой.
I'm not young anymore.

QUIZ #8

Use arrows to match the corresponding translations:

a. grass

b. pastry

c. tea

d. flowers

e. cheese

f. cash

g. seaweed

h. tent

i. footwear

j. drum

k. lumberjack

l. doll

m. luggage

n. decoration

o. map

p. wealth

1. барабан

2. цветы

3. богатство

4. трава

5. кукла

6. карта

7. палатка

8. сыр

9. обувь

10. выпечка

11. дровосек

12. украшение

13. наличные

14. чай

15. багаж

16. водоросли

Fill in the blank spaces with the options below (use each word only once):

Мы с мужем сейчас в отпуске. Мы отдыхаем в маленьком _____ у моря. Мы приехали сюда на _____ и остановились в частном отеле. Он не новый, наоборот, очень _____, но _____ и аккуратный. Здесь очень хорошо готовят _____, лазанью и пасту. Но больше всего мне нравится _____. Они даже делают _____ ручной работы. Мы купили их для своих друзей и родственников. _____ отеля – добрый пожилой мужчина. _____ – это его бизнес, но раньше он работал _____.

Город старый, и здесь много интересного. _____ рассказал нам об истории города. У нас замечательный отпуск, но из-за пандемии мы везде носим _____.

старый	грибы
хозяин	городе
выпечка	гости
поезде	конфеты
гид	чистый
маски	ювелиром

CONCLUSION

While there is certainly much more to say about the Russian language, we hope that this general overview will help you to understand and use the words/phrases in this dictionary, as well as your own words and phrases, as you continue your journey to bilingualism.

We would like to leave you with a few suggestions for a pleasant and fruitful language learning experience:

1. Learn what you need and what you love.

   While survival Russian is indispensable, mechanical memorization of long lists of words is not the best use of your time and energy. Make sure to focus on the vocabulary that is important and useful to you in your life. Perhaps you need Russian for work, or to visit family and friends. In this case, make sure that you focus on the vocabulary that will be useful to reach these goals.

2. Do not skip learning grammar and tenses.

   Although it is not the most exciting part of learning a language, spending some time perfecting your grammar is the key to being able to manipulate the language in the long term.

3. Use available media to practice all aspects of the language.

   Movies, music, and social media provide the opportunity to practice reading, writing, and listening at any time from your phone or your computer. Aim to spend 20 minutes a day on your practice of the Russian language in order to make good progress.

4. Practice speaking as soon as you can with a native speaker.

   You can join speaking groups in real life or online.

5. Remember: **Communication before perfection**.

   It takes years to master a language, and fluency is not achieved easily. It requires commitment and regular practice. However, if you get to visit a Russian-speaking country, do not hesitate to try to speak Russian to everyone you meet. This will give you the motivation and the confidence to carry on learning. You might feel scared at first, but do not worry, people will be kind to you!

6. Enjoy the journey!

ANSWERS

QUIZ #1

a-8. b-10. c-16. d-1. e-14. f-2. g-11. h-3. i-7. j-13. k-5. l-15.
m-4. n-9. o-6. p-12.

Сегодня маленький Матвей **грустный**. Он плачет, его лицо и **глаза** красные от слёз. **Бабушка** обещала отвести его в зоопарк. Матвей обожает животных. У него есть кролик, игуана и **хомяк**. Но они не могут поехать в зоопарк, потому что машина сломалась. «Матвей, не плачь, – просит бабушка. – Ты разбиваешь мне **сердце**. Ты мой любимый **внук**, но я не могу починить машину сама!» Матвей понимает, но не может успокоиться. Виктор Иванович – **сосед** бабушки. Он предалагает отвезти их в зоопарк на своей машине. Теперь Матвей **счастливый**! Он увидел бегемота, жирафа, гепарда и даже **льва**! Из птиц ему очень понравились ара и **киви**.

«Спасибо, – говорит бабушка. – Ваша **доброта** спасла моего внука!»

«Не за что, – говорит Виктор Иванович. – Счастливый ребёнок – это лучшая **благодарность**».

QUIZ #2

a-14. b-11. c-1. d-13. e-12. f-4. g-10. h-7. i-15. j-3. k-16. l-8.
m-5. n-9. o-6. p-2.

Мои друзья хотят **жить в палатках** на этих выходных. Они говорят, что это будет весело. Но мне не нравится эта идея. Палатки – это дискомфорт. Нужно брать с собой шорты, джинсы, плащи, а я люблю платья и **юбки**. Будет солнечно и жарко, а я не люблю такую погоду. Я люблю, когда **прохладно**. Да, там будет **озеро**, но я не люблю плавать. Я могу загорать, когда есть **крем от солнца**, но недолго. Плюс я боюсь насекомых: слепни, мухи, **комары**! А дикие животные? Летучие мыши и **волки**! А ещё мои друзья будут есть **рыбу** из озера. Но я не люблю рыбу! Наверное, я останусь дома.

QUIZ #3

a-5. b-7. c-12. d-1. e-14. f-4. g-2. h-16. i-13. j-9. k-10. l-3.
m-11. n-8. o-6 p-15.

Этот **год** самый счастливый в моей жизни: мы купили дом! Мы переезжаем через **две недели**. Возле дома есть большой **гараж** для нашей машины. Перед домом большое **крыльцо**. Здесь я буду укрываться шерстяным пледом и читать книги. Откроем **дверь**? Гостиная большая, мне очень нравится диван и **камин**. И, конечно же, **книжная полка** для моих книг! В кухне есть большая **кладовая** и духовка. Здесь я буду печь **имбирное печенье**. В столовой большой и широкий **обеденный стол** – как раз для нашей семьи. В спальне есть кровать и **комод**, но он маленький для моих вещей. В ванной есть **душ**, но нет ванны. Я очень счастлива и не могу дождаться переезда!

QUIZ #4

a-2.   b-6.   c-15.   d-16.   e-7.   f-1.   g-10.   h-13.   i-5.   j-9.   k-3.   l-11.
m-14.   n-12.   o-8.   p-4.

Мне 17 лет. Пока, школа, пока, **школьная парта**! Мне нужно выбрать профессию. **Дед Мороз** оставил под ёлкой большой красивый блокнот. Я беру блокнот и   **ручку** и записываю профессии. Мне нравится спорт, особенно **борьба**, но я не хочу заниматься этим профессионально. Может быть, фотограф? Я буду путешествовать и фотографировать пейзажи: водопады, пустыни и **вулканы**. Или я стану **пожарным**! Хотя нет, это опасно. Я буду **бизнесменом**! Я буду сидеть в офисе, и у меня будет много работников. Но офис — это скучно: компьютер, принтер, **папки**. Нет, бизнес не для меня. А может быть, я буду пилотом? Но я боюсь **самолётов**! Я знаю! Я куплю **воздушный шар** и полечу в путешествие. Но я обещал помочь маме. В саду меня ждёт **газонокосилка**, а потом ведро и **швабра**. Пока, блокнот!

QUIZ #5

a-5.   b-11.   c-2.   d-8.   e-12.   f-3.   g-9.   h-13.   i-4.   j-16.   k-15.   l-7.
m-10.   n-1.   o-14.   p-6.

Я **учёный** и работаю в лаборатории. Мои друзья фермеры. Они живут на **востоке** страны. Они пригласили меня в гости, и я с радостью согласился! Никаких компьютеров, веб-камер и других **устройств**. Только свежий воздух, природа, коровы и **курицы**. А ещё мои друзья выращивают овощи: картофель, тыквы и **помидоры**. Я купил экзотические фрукты: папайю и **ананас**. Мы встретились, пообедали, и мои друзья пошли доить коров. Я хотел момочь им, но корова ударила меня копытом прямо по голове! Я подумал, что это **затмение**! В глазах стало темно. Мои друзья вызвали **скорую**. Доктор сказал, что всё хорошо. Вечером мы сидели на крыльце и смотрели на **луну**. Мой друг играл на **гитаре**, и я забыл про случай с коровой.

QUIZ #6

a-6.   b-12.   c-1.   d-15.   e-9.   f-14.   g-16.   h-10.   i-7.   j-2.   k-11.   l-8.
m-5.   n-3.   o-13.   p-4.

Сегодня праздник – мой **день рождения**. Я не хотел большого праздника, просто **тихий** вечер дома. Я заказал устрицы и **лобстера** и хотел просто сидеть дома и смотреть **фильм**. Но утром пришли мои родители. Папа подарил мне **сотовый телефон**, а мама испекла шикарный **десерт** – торт в форме **сердца** с изюмом и **грецкими орехами**. А ещё она приготовила мой любимый **мясной рулет**.

Потом пришли мои друзья, и мы пошли в парк развлечений. Мы катались на **колесе обозрения**, ели **сахарную вату**, а потом развлекались на **игровых автоматах**. Это был чудесный день рождения! Лучше, чем сидеть дома и смотреть фильм!

QUIZ #7

a-2.   b-7.   c-12.   d-3.   e-13.   f-9.   g-6.   h-14.   i-5.   j-8.   k-15.   l-10.
m-1.   n-11.   o-4.   p-16.

Мой день начался **плохо**. Я работаю **поваром** в ресторане. Моя работа начинается рано, а живу я далеко. Поэтому утром я иду на **автобусную остановку**. У меня было **хорошее** настроение. На голове у меня были наушники, я шла, **слушала** музыку и **пела**. Поэтому я не заметила **сломанную** плитку на тротуаре! Я наступила на неё и упала. Мне было очень больно, и я даже хотела **плакать**. Я успокоилась, но мой день испорчен!

QUIZ #8

a-4.   b-10.   c-14.   d-2.   e-8.   f-13.   g-16.   h-7.   i-9.   j-1.   k-11.   l-5.
m-15.   n-12.   o-6.   p-3.

Мы с мужем сейчас в отпуске. Мы отдыхаем в маленьком **городе** у моря. Мы приехали сюда на **поезде** и остановились в частном отеле. Он не новый, наоборот, очень **старый**, но **чистый и** аккуратный. Здесь очень хорошо готовят **грибы**, лазанью и пасту. Но больше всего мне нравится **выпечка**. Они даже делают **конфеты** ручной работы. Мы купили их для своих друзей и родственников. **Хозяин** отеля – добрый пожилой мужчина. **Гости** — это его бизнес, но раньше он работал **ювелиром**.

Город старый, и здесь много интересного. **Гид** рассказал нам об истории города. У нас замечательный отпуск, но из-за пандемии мы везде носим **маски**.

MORE BOOKS BY LINGO MASTERY

We are not done teaching you Russian until you're fluent!

Here are some other titles you might find useful in your journey of mastering Russian:

- **Russian Short Stories for Beginners**
- **Russian Alphabet Made Easy**
- **2000 Most Common Russian Words in Context**
- **Conversational Russian Dialogues**

But we got many more!

Check out all our titles at www.LingoMastery.com/Russian

Made in the USA
Las Vegas, NV
31 May 2022

49606431R00109